616.85
RAN

Ranaghan, Denise

Institutional-eyes

GAYLORD

Institutional-Eyes

Institutional-Eyes

A Childhood Revisited in the Military

Denise Ranaghan

VANTAGE PRESS
New York

The accounts presented in this book are based upon the author's true life story, and those accounts, as well as the opinions, whether medical or otherwise, expressed herein are solely those of the author. Anyone seeking to explore the medical or psychological alternatives presented herein should consult their own doctor before beginning any new form of treatment.

Published by Vantage Press, Inc.
516 West 34th Street, New York, New York 10001

Manufactured in the United States of America
ISBN: 0-533-13364-5

Library of Congress Catalog Card No.: 99-96861

0 9 8 7 6 5 4 3 2 1

Dedicated to Kathleen Bain, who has been, and
continues to be, a crucial person in my life

Contents

Foreword

Institutional-Eyes is an honest, startling story of a young woman's painful encounter with the military. In addition, it is a vivid account of her journey into mental illness and into her own past—her encounter with the darkest, most frightening parts of her soul. It is also about the beginning of her struggle toward recovery, a journey that may last a lifetime.

I have served in the army myself, first as a private and then as a combat officer. In reading Denise Ranaghan's story, I can identify with the dehumanization that she experienced in the army. Individuals like Denise, who arrive at young adulthood with a fragile sense of identity, are especially vulnerable to a "nervous breakdown" under the unrelenting social pressure of the military. When that happens, they are given the diagnosis of a mental illness.

Medical illness is never as close to our core as mental illness: "I have a sore throat" and even "I have cancer" are radically different from "I feel empty, I'm terrified, and I hate myself." Medical illness is something we have. Mental illness, quite often, becomes who we are. This is nowhere more true than in the area of personality disorders. In the language of DSM-IV, the psychiatric diagnostic manual, a personality disorder is "an enduring pattern of inner experience and behavior that deviates markedly from the expectations of the individual's culture." This enduring pattern may cause impairment in thinking, feeling, relationships, or impulse control.

When Denise asked me to write this Foreword, she

wanted me to provide an overview of her main diagnosis—Borderline Personality Disorder—in words that a layman would understand. Certainly, the diagnosis of Borderline Personality Disorder was considered upon Denise's first encounter with the army's mental health system. Other diagnoses were to follow: Alcohol Abuse, Bulimia Nervosa, Posttraumatic Stress Disorder, Major Depression with possible psychotic features, Bipolar Disorder Not Otherwise Specified. I used some of these diagnoses myself, when I was Denise's psychiatrist, years after the events described in this book.

But diagnoses cannot tell a person's story. They are stereotyped, sterile abstractions, which may sometimes be put in good use. The diagnosis of Borderline Personality Disorder was helpful to me in treating Denise. It predicted some of the difficulties and the breakthroughs in our tumultuous relationship, and informed some of my efforts to help her. But a diagnosis lacks a human face and a sense of narrative. It fails to convey anything of the loneliness, suffering, emptiness, rage, longings, loss of identity, and despair that people with this diagnosis experience. In this candid book, Denise introduces us to her inner world, and gives us a sense of what it is like to live in her skin.

Over a hundred years ago, Breuer and Freud wrote that "hysterics suffer mostly from reminiscences." That was the starting point of psychanalysis, "the talking cure," a treatment that focused on the relationship between patient and therapist and on memories of the past in order to bring about understanding and healing. A century ago, in Central Europe, Denise might have been labeled a "hysteric" on the basis of her symptoms. Like many "hysterical" young women at the turn of the century, Denise carried with her into adulthood her traumatic memories of childhood abuse, of which she was incredibly ashamed. And like Freud and Breuer's most famous patient, Anna O., Denise eventually turned her gifts to the care of the needy and the sick.

So, what is Borderline Personality Disorder? Many people, myself included, believe that it is the result of an interaction between innate, genetically-mediated vulnerabilities and psychological trauma during childhood. The DSM-IV definition of Borderline Personality Disorder is a list of symptoms, all of which are echoed in Denise's story: *Frantic attempts to avoid abandonment, unstable and intense relationships, a disturbance in the sense of identity, impulsivity (which may lead to substance abuse and other self-damaging behaviors), recurrent suicidal behavior or self-mutilation, mood swings, chronic feelings of emptiness, intense anger, and transient, stress-related paranoia.*

But this list is voiceless. It does not convey the dread, the despair, the rage, and the hope of people who struggle with Borderline Personality Disorder every day of their lives. In addition, it may be used to blame the victim—to deny the contribution of an abusive or uncaring environment to bringing about an individual's symptoms.

It is here that Denise Ranaghan's book speaks out brilliantly, and tells a moving, seldom-told story: what it is like to have Borderline Personality Disorder, how it puts you at a disadvantage as you face a stressful and hostile environment, and how good relationships and reliable caregivers may help build up trust, which is essential for recovery.

—Yoram Yovell, M.D., Ph.D.
Assistant Professor of Clinical Psychiatry
Columbia University, College of
Physicians and Surgeons

Acknowledgments

I would like to extend my acknowledgment, gratitude and everlasting love to the following people:

My mother, who has been sober for the past five years and, despite her own problems, supported me while I was at my worst. She showed up for family therapy once a week for the two-and-a-half years I was in the hospital.

My five brothers and sisters: I thank them for our lives shared together, past and present. I love each of them.

My grandmother and her late husband, my grandfather, whose visibility over the years was crucial to my family's survival.

Rosanne Kilgannon, who was not afraid to be supportive of me when I was ill.

Diane McManus, my high-school English teacher, who was the first person to inspire me to write, and all my high-school teachers and coaches who went beyond tolerating me to support me for four full years. A special thanks to Sr. Rita King, then assistant principal, for not kicking me out of school.

My college professors, especially Dr. Joseph Tedesco, and the late Dr. Boyd Litzinger, who encouraged me to keep on writing.

Anne Dubois, my college counselor, who listened so patiently and who seemed like my only connection to the outside world when I was in the military. When I was a soldier in Germany; a letter from Anne in my mailbox was more appreciated than she will ever know.

Mary Jane Telford, my college basketball coach, who watched me make my own decisions, and never withdrew her support.

Mary Papicciola, who handled all my financial affairs at St. Bonaventure University.

Lt. Felicia P. Hackney, my commanding officer in the U.S. Army. She walked with me to get the help I needed when I was serving a tour of duty in Frankfurt, Germany.

Command Sergeant Major Booker, who was my CSM (Command Sergeant Major) for a period of time I spent in the military. He is a decent and sensitive individual.

My best friends, who have been there for me all along: Nilda Gardon Lindhofer, Jennifer Gilliam, Michael Bergman, Lucille DelGatto, and Dianne McCarthy.

Sister Patricia McGowan, who was kind enough to read my manuscript in its early stages.

Monsignor Robert Trainor and Father O'Day, who supported me emotionally when I got out of the army and was in deep psychic pain.

Dr. Robert Muller from the Riverdale Mental Health Association. He was my therapist for four years after my discharge from the New York Psychiatric Institute in 1993. Dr. Muller taught me how to put disappointment into perspective and he also insisted I take some of the responsibility in creating my disappointments.

Dr. Lyle Rosnich, former director of the long-term unit for persons with Borderline Personality Disorder at the New York Psychiatric Institute. He had great faith in me as an individual, despite my irrational stubbornness.

Barbara Bouley and Sharone Bergner, a dynamic team who edited my book for me during my stay at the New York Psychiatric Institute. Without their help, suport, consistency, and teamwork, this book would not be published. I could not have done it alone.

Leorra Friedman, my occupational therapist from the New York Psychiatric Institute, whose ability to be completely fair all of the time inspired me and won my trust.

Pat Smith, my recreational therapist, who took me to the best thrift shops to buy "appropriate" clothing for interviews for work in the "real world."

Dr. Judith Lewis, a special therapist from the New York Psychiatric Institute, who helped me through some of my toughest moments just by making herself available and present. Her care, concern, consistency, and dedication to me have helped me develop an inner sense of security which I wouldn't trade in for anything. I work with Dr. Lewis in therapy today.

Dr. Yoram Yovell, a therapist from New York Psychiatric Institute who also was my individual therapist during certain periods after I was discharged. I learned a great deal in my relationship with Dr. Yovell. He never refused to treat me, despite my desperate, but intolerable, behavior. He was also willing to negotiate the terms of our relationship and to repair damage done within it. He taught me a valuable lesson about boundaries.

Marydel Rosenfield and Carolyn Sapir, members of the Riverdale-Yonkers Society for Ethical Culture. Their encouragement inspired me to take the chance and publish my writing.

Larry Stephanile from Vanguard, who assisted me with my resumé, interviewing skills, and finding career opportunities over the last years.

Thomas Skelly from the Veterans Office of Vocational Rehabilitation Services who encouraged me to publish my book.

Dr. Robert Berger and Sara Berger, and their children, David and Jacob. Being a part of their family for the past six years has been a joy and an all-around, personally enriching experience.

My three dogs: Princess, Jacki Boy, and Mr. Magoo, who are teaching me the importance of unconditional love.

My three cats: Siam, Tally Girl, and Taylor, who bring me peace and comfort.

The following institutions have contributed to my growth and development: Our Lady of Angels, Bronx, New York; St. Eugene's Grammar School, Yonkers, New York; St. Barnabas High School, Bronx, New York; St. Bonaventure University (the Higher Education Opportunity Program), Allegany, New York; United States Army; 97th General Hospital, Frankfurt, New York; Kingsbridge Veterans Hospital, Bronx, New York; Blue Hill Hospital, Maine: New York State Psychiatric Institute, New York, New York; Veterans Office of Vocational Rehabilitation, New York, New York; Teachers College, Columbia University, New York, New York; Columbia Presbyterian Hospital, Neuro12, New York, New York; Riverdale Mental Health Association; A. K. Rice Institute of Group Relations.

Institutional-Eyes

One

Arrival in Germany

PLATOON ATTENNNN-UN! LEEEEFT FACE! SPREAD TO THE LEFT . . . MARCH! DOUBLE ARM INTERVAL . . . MOVE . . . AT EASE . . . FEET TOGETHER ARMS DOWN . . . ROTATE YOUR HEAD TO THE LEFT . . . BEGIN!

I unloaded my gear from the green army bus in front of the 596th Military Police Battalion. The company next door was having a Physical Training formation. It looked and sounded strange to me, even though I stood in many such formations in training. I was just back from a month's leave, still new to the military, and somewhere in my hopeful mind, I was dreaming that Permanent Party was going to be a whole different world from Basic and Advanced Training. My mind told me, *When you get out of training, being in the army will be just like any other job.* But my mind often lied to me.

I wrestled with my luggage until I got it all inside the door, one big duffle bag on a pushcart, one huge suitcase with wheels that didn't turn, a smaller over-packed suitcase, and a back-pack stuffed with books. All of this for two weak arms to manage. At least I didn't have to stand in the Physical Training formation holding all my luggage off the ground until my arms felt like they were going to fall off. That's what we had to do when we got off the bus at Basic Training. If you dropped your luggage there you were ordered to drop right next to it and knock out some push-ups. I could only do one push-up—with

1

great difficulty and much pain—when I entered the military. I could do 40 by the time my military career was over.

I had arrived at the place I was to spend the next two and a half years of my life, or so I thought, my first and only duty station with the U.S. Army. I had just spent two nights at a Replacement Battalion on Rhein Main air base, a holding place for soldiers new to the country, soldiers waiting to receive a pin-point assignment. It was a miserable place. I spent the days cleaning toilets and the evenings scouring huge kitchen pots. I had no objection, or little objection, to cleaning. What I resented was being treated like one in a pack of fearful dogs who needed hard-core discipline to be conditioned to respond to violence and force with violence and force. By some paradox we were meant to become strong by being humiliated so that eventually we would turn around and fight back, that is, after our long obedient silence. But we would not, of course, fight the system. We must never fight the system which molded us; for that would defeat the purpose. This holding unit reinforced what I had learned in my naivete in basic training; that a soldier is always to respect the ranking system of the military regardless of what her conscience tells her, and that she can expect to be treated as less than human because she has not earned any rank.

I lived out of my suitcase for the two days on the air base, anxious the whole time just to get somewhere so I could settle down. When I heard my name called and received a copy of my orders to a pin-point assignment, I was temporarily relieved. *At least I was getting out of this place,* I thought. *Maybe somewhere along the line I'll experience getting treated like a human being, even though I wouldn't know how to react if that happened.* I thought entirely too highly of myself to play the lowly role of private first-class in the United States Army. And yet, on other days, I felt I didn't deserve to wear the uniform. I felt I was a ridiculous disgrace to the system.

My orders directed me to the 596th Military Police Battalion in Frankfurt, just twenty minutes from the Replacement Battalion. I was bussed to my duty station.

I lined my luggage up inside the doors of my assigned battalion. The building seemed run-down and gloomy to me, like a prison cell. Down the steps and into the basement, I spotted a bulletin board full of pamphlets on alcoholism. I didn't want to be caught looking at them so I walked into one of the offices and showed my orders to the clerk.

"Welcome," she said. "You're probably the soldier whose gonna take my place. I'm leaving in two months."

A few seconds later the commander, Lieutenant Sharples, came into the office and seemed strangely enthusiastic about having a new soldier aboard. She was clearly determined to keep me as her orderly room clerk since Specialist Lorez would be outprocessing in about two months.

"Hello there, soldier! We are so happy to see you! You'll never know how happy! Tell me you're a clerk! We need a clerk real bad down here. Lorez is leaving us soon."

"Yes, I'm a clerk, a 71 Lima."

"FANTASTIC! And we didn't even know you were coming!"

Lt. Sharples was a five-foot-two, small-boned, big-mouth black female leader with a hell of a lot of enthusiasm and energy for living. She was overpowering, a fast talker and a quick thinker. She surprised many people with her resilient attitude toward problems. Her bubbly personality and her alertness kept her in control. She always spoke to soldiers very loudly and very decisively, so

3

no one tried to manipulate her to get what they wanted. She gave you the impression that once her mind was made up about something, it was final. Her attitude confused a great number of people at different times. If you didn't know Lt. Sharples you would think she was either being sarcastic or trying to make you look foolish. That's just the way she was. My first impression of Lt. Sharples was that she was "a little pain in the ass nut with a big mouth."

Still I was confused by the hearty welcome I received. I thought it was some kind of joke. I was used to being treated like a second-class citizen with no rights because training was the only army I knew and in that army soldiers were seen but not heard. You did what you were told and you didn't murmur while doing it. Here I was with a lieutenant shaking my hand and welcoming me to the unit. This was foreign and strange. *What does she want from me?* I pondered. *Why am I here? How do I get out? From scrubbing gigantic pots and pans, cleaning toilets, and standing in formations in sub-freezing weather to having my hand shaken and being welcomed to the unit instead of being ordered to get to work . . . what is this?* I was sure she was setting me up for something.

Late that afternoon I was tossed into a shoebox of a room where some sergeant lived in the barracks. It was only a temporary placement. I understood that I'd be spending the night until they found some place to put me the next morning, but the sergeant, who was not expecting me, considered this an invasion of her privacy, and when she got off work and found me sitting in her room surrounded by my luggage, she threw a fit. Talk about yanking the fear out of someone whose stomach is already turning and whose mind is already in a state of chaos! Sgt. Babbith stood there cursing out the commander for putting someone in her room who, for all she knew, "could have been a thief and stolen all her money and property."

"It's not your fault," she shouted. "Don't feel like it's your fault. It's them. They pull this kind of bullshit all the time! I'm tired of this place! It's a shithole!"

During the middle of Sgt. Babbith's yelling and cursing out the system, which I did take personally, all the pain, loneliness, fear, anger, and despair which I had been holding in until this point came gushing out in a hysterical burst of tears and anguish. I was only a few hours in the unit, but I could take no more. How the hell was I going to make it here for two-and-a-half more years! Sgt. Babbith, who, I eventually learned, was not a nasty person by nature, but who was an alcoholic with extreme mood changes, felt responsible for my outbursts; when, in reality, it was everything that had happened up to this moment that I was crying about.

"Ah, now she's crying," she moaned. "I'm sorry. I didn't mean you. I really am sorry. Why don't you come out with us tonight and party? Come on. We'll have a good time. Alright? I don't mean you. It's just this unit that's got me down."

Sgt. Babbith was sincerely sorry, I could tell. This was just her normal way of dealing with situations such as these. I later found that she almost always overreacted to everything and then laughed about it. At these times she'd look at you expectantly, hoping you'd find her amusing too.

I thought about Sgt. Babbith's offer to go out and party and, as I did, my disastrous past flashed before me and I felt compelled to decline the offer. "No, thanks, Sgt. Babbith. I have really bad jet lag. I just want to go to sleep."

5

I did try to sleep once Sgt. Babbith left for the evening, but it was impossible. I was up all night crying into my pillow over the petrifying reality that was moving closer to my heart. As I lay there with an exhausted body and a cluttered mind which I felt I couldn't even call my own, I realized I feared for my desperate life, my inability to cope. *What is going to happen to me?* I kept screeching to myself.

Once I had fallen into a light sleep at about four in the morning, I was disturbed by a drunken female soldier who had the keys to Sgt. Babbith's room and decided to come in and entertain her boyfriend regardless of my presence. She was a belligerent drunk. I knew the signs. I had been one myself. She thought nothing of kicking my luggage all over the room to make space for herself and here boyfriend to lie down on the floor. I pretended I was asleep. She and her boyfriend got comfortable on the floor and started petting and mumbling in each other's ears. I heard the girl ask, "Who the fuck is in here?" She then decided it didn't really matter and she wasn't really interested in who was in there anyway—she had better things to do. I lay on my bed, stiff as a corpse, trying not to make a peep. A t this point I was scared of my own shadow, but somehow I mustered the courage to get up out of bed and got to the bathroom down the hall. This way they'd know I was awake and maybe they'd find some place else to hang out. I didn't say anything. I got up and walked out and when I came back they were gone. The girl returned later, by herself, and climbed up into the top bunk. Just as I was sure she was in for the night and I would get some peace, she rolled off the top bunk and smashed her head on the night table that was a few inches to the left of my head. I jumped up, thinking there would be blood gushing everywhere, and screamed, "Are you okay?"

"Shit! Fuck! Shit! Yeah—I'm all right."

She climbed back up into the bed rubbing the back of her head. I dozed off about an hour later. It was after five. Six o'clock wake-up found me with nothing but insecurities running wild and the affirmation that they were obvious to anyone who saw me.

Two
Survival

For the first time in my life, people were telling me what to do and I didn't have the freedom to rebel without some serious consequences. Or, at least, I was not comfortable rebelling in this new environment because I had been well assured in training that one does indeed pay consequences for rebellion in the military. It wasn't like being in high school when I could stand up in the middle of math class, tell the teacher she was an asshole and then get detention every Friday afternoon for two months. No, in the army it wasn't that simple. The army's way of playing with your mind was so distressing that my insatiable need for attention became satiable. There was nothing I wanted more than to go unnoticed.

My first morning started out with a 6:30 A.M. urine test. I lived in the same building I worked in, just one floor above the orderly room, All the soldiers in my unit were in the barracks hallway either lined up outside my door and one by one, being escorted to the latrine to urinate in a plastic cup while somebody watched them, or they were standing around in clusters, drinking coffee and juices, hoping that soon they would feel the urge to urinate. They all seemed to chat sociably with each other while I stood alone, feeling conspicuous and conscious of my every move. I wore the same uniform, I looked like them, but I didn't *feel* like them. I just wanted to blend right in! But just one quick glance at my face, every muscle paralyzed in place, was a dead giveaway to the state of shock I was in. A new soldier never slips into the system unnoticed. Each has to go through that initial phase where they are branded "new" and somehow, along with new, "unreliable," "incapable," and "dumb." Every soldier knows how humiliating and uncomfortable it is to walk around feeling as if "new" was painted across her forehead. And every soldier soon learns she remains "new" until she adopts, unconditionally, the ways of her fellow soldiers.

For some reason the understanding that the feelings I was experiencing were not unusual and many before me had felt the same way, did nothing in helping to ease my pain. I still, somehow, believed there was something inherently wrong with me and at the same time, something inherently unique about me which made this uncomfortable experience much more intense and intolerable than it would be for the average soldier.

Some of the girls in the unit came over and introduced themselves to me. At least I could get my name out, but any conversation after that was useless because I couldn't concentrate long enough to carry on a dialogue. The confusion brought on this defensive, paranoid attitude. I had no time to think. It seemed news traveled fast, too. Sgt. Babbith attempted to include me in the group by announcing to the others who came to talk to me, that I had a college degree from the same university her boyfriend had attended. I'm sure she did not realize how much worse that made me feel. Time after time I was confronted with the question, "Why aren't you an officer?" My feelings of inadequacy went much deeper than any feelings which arose from this question, yet those feelings of inadequacy intensified with the constant reminder that I had a college degree and should have become an officer.

9

I was wrong in thinking I'd be exempt from the urine test just because I was new. Lt. Sharples saw me sitting on the black bench at the other end of the hallway, to which I had sneaked away because there were fewer people down there.

"What are you doing down here, Ranaghan?" she asked loudly.

"Nothing," I responded, like a kid caught with her hand in the cookie jar.

"Did you go yet?"

"No."

"Well, get down there then."

"You mean I have to go too?"

"Of course you have to go. You're part of this unit."

I rose to my feet, bowed my head like a puppy, and made my way down the hallway. I was fighting to hold back the tears of anxiety from feeling controlled and stuck. I couldn't even go to the bathroom in peace anymore! I couldn't believe I was going to have to live like this for more than a day or two. *What have I gotten myself into,* I asked myself over and over again. I tried with all my strength to hold back those tears, but just the thought of someone watching me urinate was upsetting and humiliating. If only I could urinate half as much as I cried over the past few days, I'd have filled the cup to the rim and it would be over and done with. The more I thought about the invasion of privacy, the less inclination I had to go. It took me another three hours before I could produce a specimen and then I was darting for the bathroom every five minutes for the rest of the day.

My feelings of aloneness and isolation magnified over my first few days at my unit. And I couldn't even relax long enough to enjoy a meal. It got to the point where I was so consumed with fear that I could not perform the simplest tasks. I was convinced I was dumb and stupid and began to question how, in fact, I had made it through four years of college when I couldn't do something as simple as putting a list of names in alphabetical order, or run a copy of something to an office upstairs without forgetting which office I'd been told to take it to. I felt I was losing my mind; I wondered if it would be temporary or permanent. I had never felt so lost and out of touch with reality before. I was in a foreign country and no one knew who I was and no one seemed to take note of my strange behavior.

I was relieved when I found that when you come to Germany in the army, they send you to a two-week program called Headstart. At Headstart they teach you a little of the German language, plus some other basic tips you need to know to get around in the country. So Headstart took me away from my unit for two weeks. I only had to report to school, but there were some days when we got out early and I was too afraid to go back to the barracks because someone might see me and send me down to the orderly room to work. I hated so much being told what to do that I was delaying it as long as possible, running like hell. *Where to?* I didn't know. *What from?* Reality. Even though I had no idea what real reality was, I was running from my projected ill fate of army life. Fear. I lived, worked, slept, ate, urinated, showered, and breathed in fear.

11

Three
No More Escapes

Once school was finished I had no place left to run and hide. I had to show up for 6:30 A.M. physical training formations, do the exercises even if I felt clumsy doing them, and march in formation to the sound of: "Ranaghan, get in step!" Keeping in step in training was a real challenge at first. The drill sergeants didn't harass me about it too much. They seemed to be overly cautious with me, more so than they were with other soldiers, probably because I was so good at appearing to do things right. But when I was put on the spot, I could not perform. If I was ever conscious of someone watching me, I botched up from trying so hard to "impress them." I was a people-pleaser and a rebel at the same time, hating and distrusting authority on the one hand while seeking a slap on the back from them so I could feel I was a worthwhile individual.

Most of the drill sergeants and first sergeants whom I came across were not the kind of authority figures one would come to trust. Like Drill Sergeant Downes, for instance. Nobody ever knew where Private Huller disappeared to at two in the morning until one night my bunk-mate spotted her, in her sexy little nightie, creeping quietly out of D.S. Downes's office, and back to her bunk. It was strange because Private Huller was constantly being verbally abused in formations.

I always thought the girls who slept with the drill sergeants would be treated nicer, their sexual affairs functioning as a tremendous tool for them to get anything they wanted, like passes to go to the supermarket, or a few trips to the local saloon. It did seem to work that way sometimes, but more often than not, they were the ones more verbally abused and scapegoated.

From day one of military life I took every comment tossed in my direction as a personal criticism which added to my already massive inferiority complex. I felt as though there were a lot of programmed robots ordering me around, treating me like a second-class citizen and threatening me with punishment every time I protested.

Years and years of fears, anxieties and hidden feelings, buried thoughts and inhibited emotions were erupting from within me. Being under such strict control was a traumatic, unconscious reenactment of my early childhood. My father was a strict disciplinarian, but he died when I was seven. When he was alive, if I came home late for dinner (even with a good excuse), I was punished. The punishment ranged from no dessert and straight to bed after dinner, to a week or two of not being allowed to leave the apartment after school or on the weekends. On some occasions he deemed it appropriate to distribute a few good whacks with his black leather belt. Even when I wasn't in trouble, if my father was around I felt his presence and I moved and spoke with a cautiousness which wasn't present when he was absent. Since his death fourteen years prior, I had felt this freedom, this uninhibited style of expression. I was able to throw my temper tantrums and act on my violent impulses. I acted without fear of consequences. If I was angry I screamed and yelled and kicked. If I wanted to stay out past dinner hour I did so and would fix myself something to eat when I came home.

But now, in the army, it was like Daddy was alive again and I had better stuff my feelings, follow the rules and behave or else I would pay the negative consequences. Fear had returned. I was no longer in charge. The platoon sergeants were—and they made it clear that if I did not go to work I'd go to jail. And if I did not do what the other soldiers did I'd get reported to the commander to be reprimanded.

The days at 596th became longer and more unbearable. Getting out of bed in the morning became too much for me to handle. Getting dressed was a dreadful thought. My uniform was never ironed as perfectly as anybody else's. My hair was never well groomed because I always got up late. My boots were never as shiny as anyone else's. Somehow, a shoelace would always wind up popping out of the top of my boot. In basic training I'd get as many push-ups as my body could knock out before it dropped in a heap on the ground, just for an untidy shoelace. There was always a piece of my uniform that wasn't right. Sometimes I'd forget to wear my belt, sometimes I'd forget to string my dog tags around my neck. On the one day out of the week that they'd check our wallets in formation to make sure we had our identification cards, I'd forgotten mine.

How petty it seems now to consider these details a basis for declaring my life unmanageable, but these were just the outward manifestations of an unbearable inner state of dysfunction. It was not so much the act of forgetting the ID, or the belt, or the dog tags, but it was the anxiety I experienced, the rip-roaring chaos which stirred inside of me which caused and perpetuated the unusual frequency of these daily occurrences. And it wasn't as though I didn't care. I wanted to do things right. But being the one singled out every morning in formation only served to cripple me further, leaving me at first feeling foolish, then depressed and then finally unable to care at all, disconnected from my world and my environment.

I was beginning to lose all forms of the military courtesy which had been instilled in me in training. Every time I was told to do something I grew suspicious and thought I was being taken advantage of. My duties as the Orderly Room clerk included many different chores, but I was so guarded that I never did any job correctly. I couldn't understand why I should be a messenger, running errands up to the first floor just because the first sergeant told me to do so. Because of my preoccupation with the motives of authority figures, I delivered messages to Office 305 when I was supposed to be delivering messages to Office 310. The more I was told what to do the more I resisted, especially when the orders came from a first sergeant who didn't seem to me to be much of an example for me to follow. Lt. Sharples didn't care for him much either and she was the new commander, having arrived only a few weeks before me.

He didn't last long as 1SG, only a couple of weeks and then a new one rolled in. I still had it in me to feel relieved. If I was going to be working as the Orderly Room clerk than I wanted to work with someone I could respect. Maybe 1SG Conners would be such a person.

But 1SG Conners turned out to be a hard-core strict disciplinarian who, if he had any feelings at all, had them buried deep within. He was born to be a soldier, a large man with light brown hair and big, scary (scary because they effortlessly pierced through my body when he looked angrily at me), alert green eyes to match his uniform. He also possessed some not so nice mannerisms. 1SG Conners used to pick his nose and pass gas without any thought or restraint and regardless of who he was in the presence of. I suppose he figured everyone did it in private anyway so why not make it public. One day I was sitting at the typewriter just in front of his desk when he exploded wind, loud as a firecracker. I was embarrassed when he did this, embarrassed for someone else's behavior. This burden I learned to take on in grammar school where the nuns made me feel guilty for laughing at something one of my classmates did which displayed improper manners, like burping, or shooting a rubber band at the back of Sister Mary Francis's head. We'd all laugh and get in trouble for it! "You would laugh at something like that! You're as bad as he is, you idiot! God's watching, you know." One time my classmate, Matty, managed to sneak out of the classroom without Sister Mary Francis noticing. He went down to the bathroom and came right back in. He was halfway down the aisle and Sister Mary Francis turned around from the blackboard and caught him. "Matthew!" she screamed. "What are you doing out of your seat! Don't tell me you left this classroom! *WHERE WERE YOU?*"

"I had to go to the bathroom, Sister," he answered so innocently. The whole class started giggling. Sister Mary Francis got so angry and then she came down and stood in front of my desk and addressed me: "Miss Ranaghan, you sit right behind him. You must have seen him get up and leave this classroom. And you didn't say anything?"

"Sister, I was reading my book," I said. And she hollered in my ear, "Nonsense! Nonsense!"

With First Sergeant Connors I felt responsible and guilty by association, guilty just for being around.

It was in no time at all that Lt. Sharples and Sgt. Marx, the only two other people who worked in the office, were fully aware that something with me wasn't right. I was a problem. I demanded to leave work at precisely five o'clock because that was what time civilians left work. I was determined to turn my job as a soldier into a civilian job because it was easier for me to cope believing I was a civilian rather than a piece of government property. It didn't work very well. I always wound up leaving work at their time, not mine. It seemed outrageous to me to get to work at 6:30 A.M. and not finish till six at night, especially when I had no personal interest in my job. *What about my personal life?* I thought, even though I had no personal life other than suffering in isolation. I was friendless. I was truly a young lost child in a foreign country, being ordered to put on a uniform each morning and appear at work. I could not attend any social gatherings, not because I had arrived at the full realization that I was an alcoholic, but because I had too much pride and didn't want to ruin my eight-months-without-a-drink, white-knuckling-it record. And I knew I could not socialize without being under the influence.

My ego kept me from taking a drink to escape this army routine so it did serve a good purpose in my life after all. Anyway, had I wanted to go out and drink, I would have had no one to go with. I had a roommate whom I experienced as "militarized" and unwilling to entertain a new soldier. She had a strong personality. There was a feeling in the air that the room we shared was hers because she was there first. I was nervous walking on her highly shined floor. She once blew up at me for being so careless as to leave a dab of peanut butter on top of the refrigerator counter. She accused me, in a most abrupt and explosive manner, of being terminally careless and sloppy.

No major external catastrophe had occurred yet. But when you're really bad on the inside it doesn't matter what's going on on the outside. Every encounter, small or big, good or bad, becomes a source of turmoil and each new problem causes further withdrawal from the world in which one lives. I did not fit in. I observed myself as a helpless observer. I watched my insides grow further and further away from the outside, reality. And I began to feel trapped, a prisoner of my own deteriorating mental state.

Four
Barely Hanging On

Saturday was here. What a relief. I had made it through a few days' work, but it was no easy chore and I doubted that I could ever do it again. I spent most of Saturday worrying about how I would manage to make it through work on Monday without being humiliated or paralyzed.

This particular Saturday, I managed to get myself out of my room. I showered in the shower room, an abnormally stressful act because five people could take a shower at one time and there was nothing separating the showers. It was like being back at camp when I was in the third grade. The lack of privacy was an issue there too. I had been awkward and grossly inhibited showering while under the constant observation of the camp counselors and while fellow campers showered alongside of me. Now I was showering in the barracks and one other girl was in there with me. I cleaned myself with extra care because I was afraid she was watching me and would run and tell everybody that the new girl didn't clean herself properly and didn't use a washcloth. I also took the shower farthest from her, and hoped she wore glasses.

I got myself out of the barracks pretty quickly and found my way to the military shopping center in town. Along the way, I asked three Germans to give me directions, but of course, they didn't speak English. I was so busy looking for signs and posts that I didn't pay any attention to what was in front of me. I ran into a steel pole about four feet high. I was hit hard. Two Germans who were walking by laughed. I screamed, but continued down the street trying to regain my composure by pretending it didn't hurt, as though the crash never happened. The wound was very painful, but I kept walking, looking cool on the outside, feeling dumb and humiliated on the inside. I started to cry, more because of my aloneness than because of the physical pain I was feeling. I was losing the small amount of hope which I had managed to hang onto, for survival purposes.

After about two hours I finally found refuge in the corner of a Burger King in the main shopping center in Frankfurt. A walk to this PX usually takes twenty minutes. I didn't really care that my walk had taken six times as long. The PX was familiar and safe and that's all I wanted. I was among Americans in an American fast-food joint. I ordered a salad, fries, and a Coke, and I nursed a cup of coffee for two hours. I didn't know what else to do and I wasn't ready to venture back out there to find my way back to Gabes Kaserne where my barracks was. It was cold outside and very gray. It was the type of day one should spend curled up in front of a fireplace with a good book or a good lover—whichever was available.

I felt my fear was as plain and easy for the man standing behind me in the Burger King line to read, as it was for me to feel. I wished I had known one person, just one, whom I could ask for help, just one person who might be able to curb my terror and loneliness. There were plenty of soldiers in military uniforms, but no faces looked familiar to me. I wanted to curl up in the corner of Burger King and vanish into the wall.

Before long, Monday arrived, and it was time to start another dreadful week. I had the opportunity to go to lunch that Monday afternoon with Anne, the girl who was training me for the job in the orderly room. Anne shared with me how she had just come out of treatment. "I'm still sort of self-conscious about it," she said, "but I just got out of the hospital. I was drunk and tried to commit suicide. They sent me through the six-week Residential Treatment Facility. I go to AA meetings all the time now."

AA clicked in my mind. I had gone to one meeting in the states with my mother because she had just come out of treatment and she was working on a program of recovery. I was in high school back then. I remember sitting and listening to all the people sharing about where they came from and what their life was like. I was amazed when my mother spoke up and said she used to have a pint in her purse at all times. I knew she drank heavily, but I never knew she had a bottle with her all the time.

Somehow—I suppose through my desperate attempt to grab at anything that seemed like it could possibly help me—I asked Anne if I could go to an AA meeting with her.

"Sure," she said. "There's one tonight on Miles Kaserne. I'll pick you up about 7 P.M."

I felt a tinge of relief for the first time since I had arrived in Germany.

At the meeting that night I didn't say a word; just sat and listened to people introducing themselves as alcoholics and then explaining some of the frightening experiences they went through during their drinking days. I immediately related to both the insanity of the situations in which these people found themselves, and the feelings they experienced when they tried to stop drinking. People talked about losing jobs, waking up in places and not knowing how they got there; violent fits they went into when they drank; how they managed to alienate themselves from every single person they cared about; and how they realized, when they dried out, that they were paralyzed when it came to understanding how to live, how to manage to make it through even one day at work.

I got to thinking about some of my own drinking escapades. There was that time when I was sixteen and had to be dragged out of the bar by my coat collar because, when some girl pushed through the crowd to get by and she brushed my shoulder, I curled my fist, turned around and belted her in the face. Then there was that morning I woke up on a park bench, with amnesia, dirty, cold, stiff, bruised, and aware at first of the noise of a little old lady's shopping cart rolling over the cracks in the sidewalk. Then there was the morning after my high-school graduation party when I woke up in the fetal position on the floor outside my fourteenth-floor apartment. I woke because Annie, my sister, was on her way out to church and I fell through the door when she opened it. And the morning I woke up naked, in a strange bed, not knowing where I was, how I got there, or who the men talking in the kitchen were. *Had I slept with them?* I wondered. *What happened? Where were my clothes?* Or the night in college when, with superhuman strength, I ripped the doorknob off my dorm-room door, the night I threw my roommate's clothes out the window for no known reason; the night I woke up on the floor in the dorm bathroom, with stiff hair and dry blood caked on the back of my neck. And there were many other less dramatic nights, but ever so emotionally painful because even though I knew that while my feelings were hard to bear, they intensified when I drank. And even with the knowledge that it got worse when I drank, I continued to drink. Many nights I lay my head on my pillow and prayed: "Now I lay me down to sleep, I pray the Lord my soul to keep. If I should die before I wake, bless you Lord, it's no mistake!"

At the AA meeting I was too petrified to open my mouth and say a word. When they went around the table and it was my turn to introduce myself, I introduced myself as Denise. I was the only one in the room who didn't follow my name with the phrase "and I'm an alcoholic."

It was awkward with Anne nudging me after the meeting ended, telling me to mix and mingle in the social hour that followed. I wasn't up to that. I was ready to race out the door as soon as we finished the prayer at the end of the meeting. No one made an effort to speak to me, though everyone seemed friendly. They all said hello and smiled. They seemed to be contented, laughing and talking about themselves to each other. I wondered where they got the free spirit from. Everyone else seemed comfortable and relaxed and I felt like a piece of cardboard.

The AA meeting was the first of a two-month series of meetings which added to my emotional turmoil. The more I listened at meetings, the more confused, scared and angry I became. But I continued to attend, sometimes flying out the door before the meeting ended, sometimes staying for the whole thing. Many nights I'd cry my way home, often stopping behind a building to sit down and sob, wishing someone understood what I was going through. My fear wanted so badly to get out and be talked about, but my anger kept me from turning to another human being.

I rode out this painfully crippling state. And through it all there was a small voice inside me, telling me I couldn't possibly be an alcoholic because I hadn't had a drink in eight months. What a paradox! I kept going to meetings because I heard things that rang true for me, yet I told myself alcohol could not be blamed for my present difficulties. I clearly remember one morning at work when a staff sergeant asked me to rip some pages out of a roster book and throw them in the garbage. It took me *four hours* to do it and there were only fifteen pages in the book! And when I was done I was done only because I was frustrated and angry and gave up—not because I was finished. I sat in the chair next to the sergeant's desk and played with the papers, riffling them, trying to figure out the best way to get the task done. I was thinking that there must be something else to it besides tearing the pages out of the book. My mind was unreliable, darting from one thought to another, jumping around and not able to concentrate on any one thought at all, no matter how important or trivial it was.

On another morning I imagined that every person who came through the doors of the orderly room was there to see me because someone had told them how crazy I was, and they were coming to test me. Whatever I was asked I perceived as a test to see how I would respond. And every time I responded I was sarcastic, defensive and nasty. These incidents had nothing to do with the influence of the substance alcohol.

I was having trouble sleeping at night now. My roommate was spending some nights off post with a friend of hers and I was in the room alone. I left the light on to sleep at night. Many nights I was plagued with thoughts of people being outside my door, and of people playing tricks on me, like making a squeal or slapping noise outside my door and then running away when I came to answer it. Of course there was never anyone there when I'd slowly and cautiously crack the door to see who the invaders were. I was scared to leave the window open for fear someone might come through it. I lay on my bed at night, stiff as a corpse, not daring to move because I was scared of the noises I myself would make. I left the radio on all night long because I was afraid of the silence. And I had a terrible fear of someone creeping up and attacking me in the middle of the night. I was sure people wanted to harm me. They were after me. This military unit I had joined was really a huge conspiracy, I thought, and they were conspiring to drive me insane.

Meanwhile, sitting in the back of my overactive mind was the memory of a night at college when I had gotten so drunk and violent that I beat up Val, the one friend I trusted the most. The fight was over who was going to sit in the front seat of the car on the way home from an after-hours party. We were all drunk, including our driver, Alice. Rather than arguing with Val over the front seat I took my full glass of beer and threw it in her lap. She retaliated with an anger I had never seen in her before. Her anger infuriated me even further and I began swinging at her. I pulled her hair and scratched at her face. The fight was broken up quickly; I can't remember if Val harmed me at all, but I do remember that she rode in the front seat of the car and I continued to yank at her hair from the back. She was screaming at me just the way my sister used to scream when we had fights: "You really are crazy, you know that! You're insane! Don't you ever talk to me again! I hate your guts, you asshole!" Drunk Alice was driving and she was screaming and crying because she couldn't drive with all of us yelling back and forth.

When we got back to the dormitory that night I tried to talk to Alice. I wanted her to tell me that it wasn't all my fault and that I wasn't crazy, but Alice ran headlong up the stairs away from me and into her room where she locked the door behind her. Desperate to get someone to be on my side, I begged her to slow down, wait and listen. But she was too frightened. I didn't blame her for being afraid. With absolutely no provocation I had thrown a quart bottle of vodka at her head one night. Luckily, I was so drunk that my aim off and it just skinned the top of her hair and smashed on the wall a few feet behind her.

I had gone into my room that night. My roommate, the quiet country girl, was not at home. I wanted to die. I had lost my last friends and I felt I had nothing to live for. One by one I had eliminated the people in my life whom I had been close to. I took all the medicine in the bathroom cabinet, mostly for colds, and I lay down on my bed and prayed not to wake up in the morning.

But I woke up in the afternoon, with a massive headache and a sense of failure for not having succeeded in my plan of action. I was angry at God for allowing me to live. I didn't want to face the people I had hurt. I didn't want to have to tell everyone I was sorry again only to repeat my actions the next time I got drunk.

Yet here I was in those same shoes just a few years later. I was in the military instead of in college and though I was not drinking, I still felt crazy. Val was right, I *was* crazy. I was feeling the same way I felt when I drank—hopeless, alone, and wanting to die. I didn't want to be in the army and I had no idea how to proceed with my life.

Five
Complete Withdrawal

Lt. Sharples had been observing me since I arrived at the unit. She had tried to be patient when I responded to her without saying "Ma'am," which is common military courtesy when speaking to an officer. Once she corrected me by kindly saying "I'd like it if you threw a 'Ma' am' in there once in a while, okay, Ranaghan?"

I looked at her, dumbfounded. I wasn't angry, because we had just been talking for a few minutes; it had been a pleasant conversation that I didn't want to ruin with my usual reflexive retaliation. Lt. Sharples had been nothing but kind to me since I had arrived at her unit in January. At first, I resented that she had authority over me. I felt that anyone who had more rank than I did had the power to abuse me, to control me for the sheer ego trip. I guess she sensed this fear of mine. She was very patient with me.

It all happened so quickly, but that dreaded morning had finally arrived. I reported to work at my usual time. I was no less paranoid now than I was the first day I arrived at the 596th. The morning lasted forever. I knew from the minute I got out of bed that I was finished. I hadn't an ounce of energy left to cope. The phone rang in the orderly room. I answered it. I didn't know the answer to the question the person on the other end of the line asked, something about stats. *Stupid me, not knowing the answer to the question,* I thought. But I didn't know what to do about it so I said in a snappish tone of voice, "I don't

27

know what you're talking about," and hung up the telephone.

I sat at the desk in the office and did nothing for a very long time; I didn't care anymore if people thought something was wrong with me or not. I didn't care anymore if I was alive or dead; I was beyond reach.

After two hours of entering and leaving the office, the staff sergeant asked me on one of his returns if I could type up a list of names in alphabetical order. This proved to be totally confusing to me. It took me a very long time to do this routine simple task. Then someone else came in the office and noticed there was a puddle of water on the floor. A refrigerator was leaking in Lt. Sharples's office, which was just inside of the office I was sitting in. It was an office within an office. A few more people came in and said something to me about the puddle of water, but I didn't make any move to clean it up, even though I was a worker in the office. *These people are just pointing it out to make me mad,* I thought. *Maybe one of them even put it there on purpose, to see if I would clean it up.* It never crossed my mind that the puddle was unrelated to me personally and it was my responsibility to clean it up because it was there—four feet from my desk and right in the middle of the office.

Finally Lt. Sharples came out of her office and said something about the puddle and I immediately went to get some towels to clean it up. I cared about Lt. Sharples. At least I was conscious of that—but I did not care about anything else. Soon my state of not caring turned into a state of deep rage. I was cleaning up the water on the floor and a huge black man in uniform came in, stood over me, crossed his arms over his chest and hollered: "What do you think you're doing, soldier?"

28

"What does it look like I'm doing? I'm cleaning up the water!"

He turned and walked out of the office. *This is another set-up just to see how I will react,* I thought. Now I had attracted so much attention to myself that people were actually testing me to see how I responded to different situations. That man petrified me with his bigness and his nastiness toward me.

I left the office after Lt. Sharples told me I would be working at the GI party after lunch. I went to my room, lay on my bed and shook. I couldn't believe I was in the army and had to take orders and clean toilets and carry weapons and wear caps on my head! *How did I ever make it through training!*

Training felt different. I was numb. I don't think I fully comprehended my whereabouts. It was as if I was in a fog, a state of denial which I needed to be in to survive. I was better than functional in Basic Training. I was superhuman. I remember we had very little free time; none at all, in fact, for the first few weeks. Once in a while we were given a free half hour here and there to write letters home, but I would spend the time running around the buildings in the area we were restricted to.

One evening we got home from a full day at the range. We'd had an hour of physical training at 0500 hours, then we marched to the range with all our equipment on our backs, spent the day learning how to zero our weapons, and then marched back to the company. The drill sergeants told us to unload our equipment, turn in our weapons, and take an hour of rest before we marched to dinner. Most of my peers slept, wrote home, or sat outside the barracks smoking and socializing. But I decided to go for a three-mile run around the area.

I had done everything I was told in training, all the

while trying to ignore my inner bedlam. I carried the pressure that only a striving perfectionist is familiar with. I and all the other soldiers in my platoon were in the same boat at these training sites. We were all bullied and yelled at and picked on. But now I was alone and on my own. Everyone else in my unit seemed well adjusted and settled down. It wasn't like I had a bunkmate to discuss the struggles and humiliations of the day with, knowing she had a list of her own complaints to relate.

I reported as directed for the GI party at 1300 hours (1 P.M. civilian time). We had to clean the bathrooms, shower rooms and hallways. The terrible morning was still fresh in my mind. I went into the GI party ready to crack and that didn't take long at all.

Everyone looked busy cleaning. As I sat hunched over on the bench in the shower room, I thought how I really wanted to do something, to pitch in, but there was nothing to do because everyone else worked so well together without me. Then a sergeant walked up and told me to start scrubbing down the walls in the shower room. I didn't like this sergeant. She looked like the type of person who liked to annoy people and boss them around. (Of course, most people in the army looked like that to me.) When she told me to start scrubbing the walls down, I thought she was trying to humiliate me; so, in a reaction of anger and panic, I took the cleaning sponge and the cleanser and flew out of the shower with it. I ran down to the bathroom and put the supplies in the cabinet, slammed the door shut, went straight to my room, and locked myself in.

My room was on the same floor as the GI party. I heard the voices in the hallway as I sat on my bed. I was withdrawing inside myself, going to a place where nobody could hurt me, no one could touch me and no one could tell me what to do. It didn't matter anymore. Nothing mattered . . . I slid off my bed and crawled to the corner of my room, scrunching myself up in a little ball with my head against the locker and my arms tightly wrapped around my legs. I buried my head between my knees and my chest and I stared straight down. I was safe there, catatonic. My back was up against the front bedpost, my shoulders curled in toward my knees. *I will stay here and be left alone,* I thought. I was immovable, untouchable, unreachable.

My roommate Mary came in and asked me what was the matter. I heard her, but I did not respond to her questions. I didn't budge or peep. She didn't waste too much time running down the hallway to get the squad leader and the platoon sergeant. Seconds later, they barged into my room and stood over me. I could see their big black combat boots out of the corner of my eye.

The squad leader yelled at me: "Ranaghan, get up and get back to work right now!"

No answer from me.

"Ranaghan, did you hear me? Get up and get back to work RIGHT NOW. Get back to work! You are AWOL, you know, if you don't get back out there and start working like everyone else. You are absent from your appointed duty section."

No response from me.

The platoon sergeant jumped in next: "Ranaghan, if you don't get up and get back to work you are going to jail. Do you understand me, Ranaghan? Do you?"

No response from me.

"Maybe you don't hear me right, Ranaghan. I said you are going to jail if you don't get up right now and get to work. We'll have to have them come and take you away

31

in a straitjacket. Would you like that better than getting up and going back to work on your own?"

No response from me.

I had heard every word that was being said, but I was long past the point of caring about what happened to me. I had nothing left; nothing to fight with and nothing to live for. I had gone inside myself, removed myself from reality. I had heard, but I was unable to respond, even to keep myself from being sent to jail. I was safe. It was safe to be where no one could reach me.

The squad leader jumped in again.

"Ranaghan, you're really pushing your luck. Either you get up now or we're going to get the commander. Do you want us to get the commander? You'll really be finished then. She's not gonna take this shit from you. This is your last chance. Get up NOW, Ranaghan!"

Still no response from me, not even a budge. I hadn't moved a limb the whole time I was on the floor scrunched up. I heard the platoon sergeant say to the squad leader, "Come on. Let's go get the commander. She's not moving."

They left my room and slammed the door behind them. I was alone in the room. This was a relief, but I still did not move. I didn't want to move. I felt like I could have stayed there forever. I would have very much appreciated being left there alone, indefinitely.

Not more than five minutes later, I heard footsteps entering my room. It sounded like quite a few people, and the footsteps were loud so I knew it was military personnel. The thump of the combat boots was familiar. People were standing behind me in my room, and for a short while no one spoke at all. Then Lt. Sharples, very slowly, walked up closer behind me, and very softly said, "Ranaghan, it's just me, Ranaghan."

Lt. Sharples sat down on the floor in front of me with

her back against my wall locker, mimicking my position. She put her arms around her knees and curled up, not quite as compact as I was, a little more relaxed. She began to speak to me in a tone one would use with a child who was crying and needed comforting:

"What's the matter, Ranaghan, huh? What's the matter? Come on, you can tell me? I'm your friend, Ranaghan. What's the matter?"

Lt. Sharples had taken her army jacket off so the rank wouldn't affect our dialogue. I didn't respond anyway. Lt. Sharples continued. She slowly worked herself closer in proximity to me, to the point where she could touch my finger gently without me scrunching up farther against the bedpost. I remained unresponsive, but I was not withdrawing further. My condition was stabilized. I was softening up inside. I felt this woman really did care. I wanted to crawl up in her lap and be held like a baby. I wanted to wrap my hands around her breast, put my lips to her nipple and suck until I was satisfied. I wanted to be safe. I wanted to go back and start my life over again. I wanted the nurturing I never received. I wanted to be loved and treated as someone special. *And I was so ashamed of myself for having these feelings. . . .*

"Ranaghan, can you tell me how you feel? Ranaghan, it's okay! You don't have to be scared. Are you scared, Ranaghan? Don't be afraid. No one's going to hurt you. You can talk to me, Ranaghan. Can you tell me what's wrong?"

Lt. Sharples and I were the only two in the room now. The other military people had walked out and closed my door gently behind them.

"Ranaghan, can you lift your head up a little bit? Lift your head up a little. Can you do that, Ranaghan? Lift your head just a bit for me?"

33

I did not budge. My hands were in front of my knees, my right hand gripping my left wrist and my left hand sort of hanging loose. Lt. Sharples played with my pinky as she spoke. I did not resist. Inside, I was beginning to feel like reaching out and clinging to her, as she had reached inside of me, but I was too afraid to let the inside come to meet the outside.

Lt. Sharples did not threaten me. She patiently sat and talked to me for about an hour. All the time, I showed no sign of improvement, other than that I was not withdrawing further as I had done when the platoon sergeant and the squad leader were yelling at me.

"Ranaghan," Lt. Sharples said, "I'm going to go away for a minute. Will you stay right here? Ranaghan, I promise I will be right back. Will you stay here?"

I responded for the first time. I nodded my head slightly. I really would have begged her to come back if I could have spoken. I didn't want to be left alone anymore. I wanted to be taken care of. Lt. Sharples was very much encouraged by my response. In a high voice, high but not loud, she said, "Good, Ranaghan. Good. I will be right back. Don't you go anywhere."

I sat there while Lt. Sharples scooted off. But I knew she was coming back, so I felt safe and secure. I still did not move though, even after Lt. Sharples had left the room, and my bones were becoming stiff and cramped.

Lt. Sharples came back a few minutes later and sat down on the floor again. "I'm back. You see, Ranaghan? I told you I'd be back. Now, Ranaghan, can you look at me? Just lift your eyes up and look at me. Can you do that, Ranaghan?"

I didn't do it. Lt. Sharples persisted, determined to get me to look at her, and after a while, I was able to look at her chin, though I could never look her straight in the eye. I was terrified, shaking at the effort it took just to look at her chin. My head was slightly lifted after having been tucked behind my knees and I was looking in her direction. My head was still tilted sideways and fear welled up in my eyes as I stared without blinking.

"Ranaghan, who do you want to talk to now? Is there someone in particular who you want to talk to, someone we can call who will come and talk to you?"

I was thinking silently. The only person I trusted was Bettie, a woman I met in AA who peeled me off the bathroom floor during The Church of Christ Saturday night Alcoholics Anonymous meeting. When my turn to speak at the meeting had come around, I cried my way through the blurted sentence, "My name is Denise, and I don't know if I'm an alcoholic and I hate the army." Bettie took me out for pizza after she got me out of the bathroom and she had a confident way about her that made me believe she could help me. Bettie returned to her hometown, Phoenix, Arizona, about two weeks after I met her. She was the only one I trusted and I didn't have her number so I couldn't call her. I felt she deserted me. She abandoned me by severing the only human connection I had.

"Is there someone you would like to talk to, Ranaghan?"

I shook my head slightly from side to side.

"Nobody, Ranaghan?"

I shook my head more definitely, almost as if I was getting angry.

"Do you want to talk to the chaplain, Ranaghan?"

I nodded my head in an unmistakable no. I didn't know the chaplain. Why would I want to speak to another army man I did not know?

"Did you want to speak to me, Ranaghan?"

I did not respond.

"Do you want to talk to me, Ranaghan?" Lt. Sharples repeated.

I slowly moved my head up and back down again, one time.

"You do want to talk to me, Ranaghan?"

I shook my head again.

"Ranaghan, do you think you could sit up on the bed and we can talk? You'd be more comfortable on the bed, Ranaghan."

I was overcome with fear and my heart started pounding. I really didn't want to move. A tear trickled out of my right eye and slowly rolled down my cheek. I started to realize a little of what I had done; I knew that I had totally lost control and I was a few steps beyond desperation.

"I will help you, Ranaghan. I will help you get up. We can do it together. Can we give it a try? It's okay, Ranaghan. It really is okay. You will be fine."

Lt. Sharples went to take my hand and I quickly and firmly withdrew it. I stiffened up and withdrew further. My whole body became stiff, starting with the hand she had touched. I did not want to get up. But I did not want Lt. Sharples to leave, either.

"Ranaghan, it's okay. I will help you. I am your friend. I will not hurt you. Just give me your hand and we will get up and sit on the bed. That's all, Ranaghan. Can we do that? We can get on the bed and then we can talk. Can you hear me, Ranaghan? Are you with me?"

I began to move my finger around a little bit. I uncurled my tight fists and very slowly inched my hand out, away from my body, toward Lt. Sharples's outstretched hand. Lt. Sharples took hold of my hand, my head still cast downward. I was ashamed of what I had done—I was coming around. I slowly raised myself to a standing position. Lt. Sharples walked me a few feet and very gently placed me in a sitting position on the end of the bed. My head remained bowed, still not wanting to look at anyone, especially myself.

"Ranaghan." Lt. Sharples sat next to me on the bed and held my hand. "Ranaghan, can we talk now? Do you want to tell me what's wrong?"

I nodded my head.

"You do know what's wrong? Can you tell me what's wrong, Ranaghan? I'm listening. I want to help you, but you have to talk to me for me to help you. What's wrong, Ranaghan?"

I answered slowly and quietly. "I think I'm an alcoholic, but I'm not sure."

"You think you're an alcoholic? Well, I think I know who can help you. Can you wait here again, Ranaghan, while I go away for a minute. I will be right back. Sit back on the bed and wait till I get back. Can you sit back on the bed, Ranaghan?"

I was getting better because I moved back and rested my back against the wall with my legs stretched out horizontally across the bed, while my feet hung over the edge of the bed. Lt. Sharples left the room, and returned about five minutes later. She looked excited. I was happy to see her excited because it made me believe I was going to get help. I wanted to believe that Lt. Sharples had the answers and because she seemed so up, I thought maybe she did know how to help me.

"Ranaghan, I have a friend downstairs whose gonna come and talk to you tomorrow. She can help you."

In my mind I thought maybe it was going to be Bettie. How could I think that Bettie was going to fly all the way over from Arizona to Frankfurt just to talk to me? She had just left a few days ago and had no idea what was going on with me.

"Ranaghan, at 8 A.M. tomorrow morning some special people are going to be here to talk to you. I will be here too, okay? You are going to stay here tonight and I will be here at 8 A.M. Will you be okay here alone tonight?"

"Yes, I will be okay."

Lt. Sharples left shortly after that. I was awake all night with my radio on, my windows closed and my lights on, wondering who was coming to see me in the morning. I was scared to get up and leave my room to go to the bathroom because I didn't want anyone to see me and I thought people were spying on me. I was existing like a frightened child, in an unprotected, evil environment.

My roommate Mary was staying at her boyfriend's. I put a Billy Joel tape in my cassette player and played it over and over again, all night long. I lay in my bed, stiff as a board, afraid to move. I was afraid when I heard any noise at all because I thought it was someone coming after me or playing a trick on me. I closed the window so that no one could climb through it and attack me; I couldn't close my eyes without the fear that when I opened them, someone would be standing over me in my room. I never went to sleep. It was a very long night.

This sleepless night I later paralled to the sleepless nights I had in childhood, when my mother's second husband, Harry, would be out at the bar and no one knew what time he was going to come storming through the door in a rage, looking for someone to vent his anger on. We knew he'd be back because he had no place else to go. It was just a matter of time. And when he returned loaded, he was apt to wake all of us six kids up and choose one to victimize with his brutality. None of us ever knew who was going to be the chosen one, either.

38

In the military, my sleepless nights were because of the fear of the unknown. In childhood, it was the same. Anything could happen over the course of one night.

Six

A Trip through the Hospital

Lt. Sharples was late that morning. I started to get worried, but I knew she would come. She'd said 8 A.M., but she didn't get there until about 8:30 A.M. When she knocked I was sitting up on my bed in the same position she had left me in the day before. I was waiting patiently. I guess my way of reaching out and expressing that I still needed help was by doing the same things I did the day before. If Lt. Sharples thought I seemed better, she might forget, the whole thing and I'd be lost again.

"Let's go now! You ready, Ranaghan?"

"Where we goin'?"

"To meet the people."

"I thought they were coming here."

"Well, we have a little change of plans and we are going to meet them. It's not far, Ranaghan. Come on."

I was suspicious of any change of plans, but I was not able to refuse now. I couldn't continue functioning in the state of mind I was in. I couldn't maintain that state even if I wanted to, because society said it was very strange to do so and of course, the military said it was unacceptable. I went along.

We drove in Lt. Sharples's little blue car. I don't know what kind of car it was. I never paid much attention to cars and brands. I never cared. I still don't, really. We rode about a mile through Frankfurt before we pulled into a parking lot where the sign read "Frankfurt Mil-Base," and another one just beneath it read "Drug and Al-

40

cohol." We walked up a ramp and through a couple sets of doors and then down a flight of stairs in a small corner of the hallway. Down there, in the basement, a man named Sgt. Houzer, a counselor for Drug and Alcohol Addiction, was waiting for me to arrive. He escorted me into his office. Lt. Sharples told me that she would be back in a little while and that if I got out of my meeting early I should meet her right there in the waiting area. I was nervous. I felt like I used to feel when my mother dropped me off at kindergarten and would leave me. Some days I just wouldn't let her go. I'd cling to the back of her leg and scream and cry until she gave in and took me home with her. The whole way home she would be screaming at me and pulling away from me, trying to get me off her, as if I was some kind of unwanted, disgusting fungus clinging onto her clothing: "You lousy little bastard! You're a spoiled little bitch! I took you all the way to school, wasted the whole morning when I could have been doing something else, and then you pull this shit! Stay away from me today or I swear I'll punch your little face in!"

Now I thought, *Lt. Sharples is leaving me but when the day is over she'll come back to pick me up.* It wasn't such a bad day that I had to wrap my arms around her leg, clinging to her to prevent her from leaving, or scream and yell until she couldn't stand me anymore. It wasn't *that* bad—but it was bad inside, very bad on the inside. I wanted "Mommy" right there with me to protect me. I had to settle for Mommy coming back when the appointment was through. I'd wait for her and she would come.

My meeting with Sgt. Houzer was very unpleasant. I didn't like him to begin with, because he had asked Lt. Sharples to leave. Sgt. Houzer was a strong, confident, domineering black man who wasted no time getting right to the point. If I didn't answer his questions immediately, he would jump right in and repeat the question very loudly. He asked me questions I didn't want to answer and he confused me. When I was in his office, it was as if I had no control over what I was saying. Words were just rolling out of my mouth, but I was not consciously choosing what I wanted to say. It was so strange hearing myself. Nothing connected; one minute I'd be talking about how I used to beat up my friends when I drank, and the next minute I'd be talking about the death of my father. And a minute later I'd be talking about how we were playing with the Ouija board one night in college and I asked it if anyone in the room was an alcoholic and it spelled my name out. I couldn't feel anything in this session with Sgt. Houzer except massive confusion. Free floating thoughts were gushing out, without seeming to belong in any particular place or even to any part of the conversation that had been initiated.

"What are you doing here today?" Sgt. Houzer asked.

"I don't know."

"What do you mean, you don't know? You must have done something that made your commander bring you in here. How did you get here?"

"I'm an alcoholic."

"What makes you think you're an alcoholic?"

"Actually I don't know if I'm an alcoholic or not. I think I might be. I did some violent things when I drank and I didn't always remember exactly what I did. . . . but I think they must have been pretty violent because no one at school ever called for me to go to dinner after the night that I think I did the violent things. . . . and then I had to ask around to find out why no one wanted to talk to me . . . and then I heard things like, 'Why would they want to talk you after last night? Denise, you should really go to the counseling center and talk to someone. People are get-

42

ting tired of taking your shit. You're a good friend, but you're crazy when you drink.' And then I remember being really angry because I felt these people were against me, setting me up because they didn't like me. I don't know what's going on, to be honest. . . . I just started going to AA meetings and the people there are really scary. They all talk about being sick. . . . I haven't had a drink in eight months but sometimes I get the urge to drink just to relax and clear up all this confusion. I can't live like this much longer. I don't understand."

"So you haven't had a drink in eight months?"

"No."

"How did you get here? What happened at your unit that Lt. Sharples brought you here?"

I shrugged my shoulders and Sgt. Houzer repeated the question much louder than necessary so I shouted back at him: "I crawled up in a ball in the corner of my room, okay?"

"Why did you do that?"

"Look, asshole, if I knew the answers to everything I'd be in your seat and you'd be in mine. You're the one who's supposed to figure out why I did it?"

He lowered his voice to a more moderate level and continued probing: "How did you feel when you crawled up in a ball in the corner of your room?"

"I couldn't move, I didn't *want* to move. I felt like I was possessed or something."

"Possessed. Possessed by what?"

"I don't know. I can't explain it. It was very strange. Maybe it was God."

"Do you think God was punishing you, or was He helping you?"

"I think I haven't got the slightest clue what He was doing! I don't know if it was God! I just can't explain it!"

Sgt. Houzer asked me a few questions about my family background. I responded, "My father died when I was seven. When I was nine, my mother met this lunatic in a bar and she wound up marrying him two weeks after she met him. He was insane, beat the shit out of her every night and beat us kids too. He stole cars, stole money—lived the life of a bona fide criminal. He split our family up because his abuse became so bad that my relatives stepped in and took us children away. We weren't even getting our meals anymore. He took all our Social Security money to the bar and pissed it away. And then had the nerve to come home and beat the shit out of us. I moved in with my aunt and uncle and lived with them for four years. They were rich—no food stamps and welfare for them. They lived in a nice, big house, had three cars and nice clothes and took vacations every year. They were professional people, you know, very hard working and determined to climb the ladder of success. I liked living with them, thought they had the answers to happy living. They were very good to me in a lot of ways. But something went rotten there, too. My aunt got jealous that my uncle and I started to spend so much time together. It really bothered her, and she blamed me for it. Then me and her became really good friends and I started to feel strange around my uncle. I always felt like he was staring at me. I was growing uncomfortable living there, and scared, really scared. Then I stopped eating. Once my aunt and uncle confronted me about my behavior and that scared me more because then I started to think I was crazy.

"Then I started throwing up my dinner every night. I pretended to them that I didn't know what they were talking about when they asked me why I was wearing a winter coat to the dinner table, and then I decided to move out. I left there and moved back to my mother's. By

44

the time I got back, the creep my mother married was gone, but my mother was still drinking all the time. I felt awful after being home a while and I wanted to go back to my aunt and uncle's, but it was too late. Months had passed and they had rearranged their lives. I called my uncle and he took me out for lunch and said he wanted me very much to come back, and that he would talk to my aunt about it. He wanted me to promise him that if I came back there would be no more of this modesty nonsense. But my aunt didn't want me to come back. My uncle said if it had been a few months earlier she would have taken me back in a second, but things had changed and I wasn't part of their family anymore. Living again with my mother made me forget most of the problems with my uncle. Sometimes I thought that maybe I had just imagined them.

"I spent the rest of my high school years drinking and throwing up. I used to get terrible headaches from forcing myself to purge, but I couldn't help it. Even if I had a little doughnut for breakfast, I couldn't relax until I threw it up. I always had headaches in those days. I would eat and throw up, eat and throw up, eat and throw up. Even at school I was throwing up after lunch. Then I'd drink on the weekends. Same kind of thing through four years of college, except I drank more than I binged and purged. There was this girl on my floor in college who used to throw up in the bathroom all the time and everyone thought she was so gross. I didn't want to be hated like her so I hardly ever threw up at school, only when I was really desperate and then I'd go to another part of the campus to use the bathroom because I didn't want anyone to see me. Then I started drinking a lot and I was a very angry drunk. I'd only binge and purge when I went home for vacations."

I was in Sgt. Houzer's office for more than half an hour. Sometimes I talked so incessantly that Sgt. Houzer interrupted me to ask me a different question. I was reluctant to answer him at first because I felt he was prying, invading my space. Yet once I started to answer, I rambled on nonstop. I don't know whether my rambling was because of the fear I sensed when Sgt. Houzer would raise his voice and seem stern, or because of my inability to make anything connect at that time. I think it was a combination of both. I had no idea why I was talking about such things to a perfect stranger. The confusion is what terrified me. I rambled and he scribbled as I rambled.

I had to sit and wait about twenty minutes for Lt. Sharples to return. While I was sitting alone, an incident from my past became so vivid it could have been a movie I was watching on the yellow wall. I stared across at it in the waiting room. I was watching me and my uncle sitting together in the Florida room pretending to be watching TV while my aunt was out at her bridge group. I was sitting on his lap, I thought, but in the movie it appeared I was sitting on his penis and I could feel its stiffness in my crotch. Then my uncle pretends to laugh at something he hears on the television. At the end of his laugh, his hand is on the back of my bra strap and he says to me, "Your bra strap is tangled. Do you want me to fix it for you, bunny?" I say yes, and I feel his hands crawl up my bare back. He unsnaps my bra and fingers crawl around the front to my breasts. His fingers slowly trace the lower part of my breasts, first one finger under each breast, then two, then three. It feels good, but something inside tells me it's not supposed to feel good because this was something one of my cousins did to me and it never felt good with him. We always had to hide when he was doing it and promise not to tell. My cousin would expose himself, too, the same part of my uncle which was now sitting in my crotch, and he would make me expose myself too, to him and his friends. Then he would rub his penis against my vagina, but it never went inside me because I was too scared. Sometimes my sister would be there, but my cousin never pushed her as far as he did me. He used her to guard the door to the attic, to make sure she would alert him if my aunt was coming.

My uncle's hands continued to wander underneath my shirt and it was taking him an awfully long time to straighten out my tangled bra strap. He finally creeps his fingers around to my back and finds the two ends to my bra strap. He snaps the two ends together and pats me on the back. Shortly afterwards we hear my aunt's car pull into the driveway and my uncle says it's time for bed. I help him slide me off his lap, he shuts the television off, then the lights, and we climb the stairs together. He says, "Good night, bunny." I return his "good night." I go to my room and he goes to his.

This memory conjured up all sorts of other memories about strange behavior I began to engage in as a kid. Because I began to feel uncomfortable around my uncle as I got older and I'd notice he'd be coming home from work drunk and stupid, I had to take precautions to keep him from undressing me with his eyes, which I felt he was always doing. I started wearing big sweat shirts around the house, and I started wearing my winter coat to the dinner table. I would undress only at night when it was very dark and I wouldn't step out of the shower stall until I was fully dressed from head to toe. I obsessively made sure the shades in my bedroom were thoroughly closed and I never crept out from underneath my covers when I slept, even if I was sweating from the heat.

47

It was during this same general time frame that my bulimia started. I was about thirteen years old. I can't remember how I discovered what I thought to be the magic trick of staying thin and shapeless. I did discover it on my own, though. No one ever told me the technique to throwing up my food. In fact, I never even knew there was a name for it until I went to college. I thought I was the only one who knew this trick, and yet I was sure my aunt knew something. I had stopped eating altogether, except for the dinner my aunt, my uncle, and I ate together each evening, which, unfortunately for me, I thought, was the one meal my aunt was around for and feverishly encouraged me to eat. I always waited to purge until she went upstairs after dinner, but then sometimes, when I opened the bathroom door after completing my ritual, she would be standing right here, staring dead straight at me. She never said anything to me, but the stare alone increased the shame I felt about my dirty little secret. I never wanted anyone to know what I was doing in the bathroom, hovered face first over the toilet bowl with my two fingers stuck down my throat for as long as it took to choke up every last morsel of food.

Meanwhile, my front teeth dug into my knuckles, sometimes so hard they cut through the skin leaving scratches, my face turned beat red from the blood rush, and my eyes painfully bulged out of their sockets from the pressure. There was something very wrong with this ritual or else I would not have felt compelled to wipe the toilet cleaner than I found it and scrub my hands and face with perfumed soap to rid myself of the smell of puke.

Finally, Lt. Sharples returned. I was so happy to see her when she came back. A heavy-set woman counselor handed Lt. Sharples the papers Sgt. Houzer had written on me. Lt Sharples went inside her office and talked with her for a short while and then she came out of the office and said: "Okay, Ranaghan, you ready? We're going to go over to the hospital now. We have an appointment with another doctor over there."

I said to Lt. Sharples, the way a child who hated hospitals would say to her mother, "I think I'm better now. We can go home. I don't need to talk to another doctor."

"Ranaghan, if you had a broken leg, wouldn't you want to go to a doctor who knew how to fix the leg . . . put a cast on it and help it to heal? It's the same thing with you. We are going to take you to the doctor who can help you with your problem. You don't want to stay confused, do you?"

"No I don't."

"Well, we'll see the doctor who is going to straighten this whole mess out, okay?"

"Yes, Ma'am. Do I have to call you 'Ma'am' with us being in civilian clothes and not military clothes?"

"No, you don't have to call me 'Ma'am' in this situation. It's okay not to."

Lt. Sharples wouldn't let me read the paper Sgt. Houzer wrote up on me. She said it was nothing for me to read right then and she wasn't allowed to show it to me.

Lt. Sharples and I talked all along the way from the Counseling Center to the hospital which was just around the corner from Gabes where I worked and lived. Lt. Sharples and I were spending time together and all our conversations were centered around me. I liked that. I saw Lt. Sharples as a strong, powerful little woman and I quickly lost any paranoia I had about what she was looking out for, other than my welfare. I asked Lt. Sharples in the car: "Do you really think the doctor can put a cast on my head and make it better?"

"Ranaghan, don't you worry. We are going to fix that head of yours, cast or no cast."

Lt. Sharples started to ask me questions about Bettie, the woman from Phoenix, Arizona, who was then in Germany with her husband, Arthur. I had mentioned earlier that I had met Bettie in an AA meeting. She had become my backbone when I first got into the program. She was a very attractive, self-assured older woman who spoke powerfully at meetings. Arthur was her handsome, charismatic husband. They were at least 50, but Bettie wore her age well with her blond hair and well-dressed appearance. I told Lt. Sharples that Bettie and Arthur had adopted me for a few weeks until they had to go back to Arizona. Now it seemed like a dirty trick. Their departure left me feeling totally stranded. They had treated me so well, had taken me to many meetings, and had always been ready to talk to me. They hadn't run away from me like the other ones in the program did. No one else at AA seemed to want to talk to me, probably because I always seemed so angry and explosive. Members would direct their conversation toward me during the meeting, but no one would approach me afterward, no one besides Bettie and Arthur.

We pulled into the 57th General Hospital and stopped at the front gate where they checked our identification cards. The gate guard saluted Lt. Sharples. She returned the salute and we drove through and found ourselves a parking space.

We walked through the doors of the hospital. I had never spent much time in hospitals before—once in a while, maybe—to visit a sick friend, but never had I stayed overnight in a hospital, except when I was born, and I didn't remember that.

We walked down the long corridor on the first floor of

the hospital. There were many people walking around: patients, nurses, doctors, civilians, Army personnel. The first floor of the hospital had a Stars and Stripes bookstore, a cafeteria, a doughnut shop, a small shopette, a barber shop, a dry cleaner, a post office, and a flower shop. It didn't look anything like a hospital. It looked like a place of business, an unusually busy place with many people walking around. But when I walked down this long corridor with Lt. Sharples, I didn't see all those shops, nor did I focus on the different people around. Instead I became acutely aware that I was in a hospital. I only saw the patients, who looked like zombies, walking around in robes and slippers. Some had arms in casts, some had crutches, some were rolling around in wheelchairs, some had patches on their faces. They looked ill to me. The one man who caught my eye was the one with a white gauze pad on the left side of his forehead just above his eye, a cast on one arm and a brace on his leg. He had on a blue, striped robe and slippers and I spotted him as we passed the door to the shopette. He was at the cash register purchasing something. For no apparent reason, when I saw him, something snapped inside me. I went berserk.

"GET ME OUT OF HERE! PLEASE GET ME OUT OF HERE! I WANT TO GO HOME! I'M NOT SICK. I'LL BE OKAY."

I stopped walking and stood there in the middle of the hallway trembling. Lt. Sharples took my hand. She was frightened because I had come on so strong, out of nowhere. We had come this far and I was ready to fly now, out the door! Some of the many people walking by turned to look at us as they passed us. Lt. Sharples took my hand and was pulling me forward now. I had my feet planted firmly on the linoleum and was struggling to pull back.

51

Lt Sharples was about half my size, but she had double my strength in all areas: mental, physical, and spiritual. As she dragged me forward with only some success, she spoke in a panic: "Ranaghan, come on. We're not going to the doctor's now. We're going to go to the cafeteria where we can sit down and talk. The doors are right there." She pointed down the hall with one hand while she held my wrist with the other.

"I don't want to go into the hospital. I'm okay! Please get me out of here! I want to go! I have to go! I don't like it here! I'm not crazy! I'll be okay! *PLEASE! OH, PLEASE LET ME GO! PLEASE. OH NO I CAN'T! I'M NOT CRAZY! PLEASE, LET'S GO NOW!*"

"Ranaghan, let's just go and sit in the cafeteria. That's all we have to do. We're not going anywhere else. Let's just go together and sit in the cafeteria. That's all."

I saw the doors to the cafeteria just ahead, but I thought it was a trick, as if when we got to the doors of the cafeteria they would turn out to be the doors to the psychiatric ward. I lost faith in Lt. Sharples. I started to think she was the enemy. *She's trying to get me to go into the hospital and look how far she's gotten me already!* I thought. *I can't believe this. She's the enemy too! She's trying to get me certified as insane! That's why she took me here. Doesn't anyone believe me? Am I the only one who thinks I'm not crazy? I sure act crazy. And if I'm not crazy then why am I spending so much time trying to convince people I'm not? If I didn't have a broken leg, I wouldn't walk around screaming, "I don't have a broken leg! I know I don't." This is not normal. I must be crazy, but I want to be crazy at home not in the hospital. Lt. Sharples knows I'm crazy and she's going to leave me in the hospital alone. That's why she won't let me read what Sgt. Houzer wrote about me. He says I'm crazy too, so they all secretly believe I'm crazy and they are trying to put me away. . . .*

"Take me home! Please take me home! Get me out of here! I don't need help anymore! Please take me out of here!"

"Ranaghan, look where we are. We are standing in the middle of the hallway. Let's sit down in the cafeteria and talk about this. It's right down the hallway."

"How do I know that's the cafeteria?" I barked at Lt. Sharples.

"Ranaghan, let's walk past the door of the cafeteria and we can look in and if it's not the cafeteria we will keep walking. We won't go in. I won't force you to do anything you don't want to do. Trust me, Ranaghan. I am not going to let you down."

Still trembling and still resisting, I walked slowly and cautiously ahead, almost as if there were steps in front of me that I couldn't see and I was afraid of falling. Lt. Sharples had my left hand and was pulling me along. She wasn't being as forceful as she had been when I first panicked. She was more like a mother now, holding her baby's hand while she learned to take her first steps. She watched and held my hand, and took me up to the doors of the cafeteria while I worked on the stepping, making sure we didn't go so fast that I'd have no control and I'd be shoved through the doors of the nutcracker suite!

I asked on the way down there, "Are you sure it's a cafeteria?"

"Yes, Ranaghan, I am sure it's a cafeteria."

"How do you know?"

"I've been here before, Ranaghan."

"How many times?"

"Oh, I don't know. You have to work at the hospital to

eat here, so not many times. Oh, and if you're a guest, you can eat here, too."

"So whose guest are you now?"

"We're not going there to eat, Ranaghan. We are just going to sit and talk for a minute. I think they'll let us in for that."

Lt. Sharples seemed to have all the right answers. At least they seemed right enough to convince me to go and peep through the door and see if it was really a cafeteria.

From the door, I could see the chow line and it looked similar to the one I stood in at our cafeteria on Gabes Kaserne. Most army chow lines look the same. They have trays and utensils at the beginning of the line and then a rail you can rest your tray on while you are waiting your turn to get served. And almost always, there are people waiting in line. The food is laid out in big trays and usually you see people pointing at what they want to eat. I recognized the scenario immediately and a sense of peace came over me. I gave up fighting, and Lt. Sharples and I walked into the cafeteria and sat at the end of a long, empty table. Lt. Sharples pulled her chair up close to mine and started to talk. First she took a deep breath as she sat down. I think maybe she was relieved we had made it to the cafeteria and also, I think maybe she was starting to get tired.

"Ranaghan, I am not going to leave you here. All we are going to do is get your medical records and then go upstairs and talk to a doctor. Then we are going to go home. Remember what I said before about having a broken leg; if you have a broken leg, you don't walk around on it broken. You get it fixed by a doctor who knows about legs."

"So you think I'm crazy and I need a shrink to fix my head. I don't! I'm not crazy! I'll be okay. We don't need to be here right now. Can't we just go home? I don't have to walk on my broken head so I should be okay."

"Ranaghan, now that we are here and we went through all we went through this morning, I think we should just talk to the doctor and then we can go home. He can help you, Ranaghan. You told me you don't want to live like you are living anymore. He can help you. We have to find out what's wrong so you can get better. If we go home now, we won't be any better off than we were yesterday when you were in the corner of the room."

I remembered myself sitting in the corner of my room. It was so safe there, but it was so scary too. Scary, because I knew I couldn't stay there forever and that none of these things were normal for a twenty-two-year-old to be doing.

As we were negotiating, I began to calm down inside and I became more aware of my surroundings. I realized that I was hungry. When you're hungry, even army chow smells good. I amazed myself and laughed at my resiliency. A minute ago I had been screaming bloody hell in the middle of a hospital hallway—now, I felt like sitting down to enjoy a tasty meal. I wanted to ask Lt. Sharples if we could have a bite to eat while we were in the cafeteria, but I never did get to it. We weren't in there more than ten minutes before we were up and on our way to the Medical Records department. I was still feeling paranoid, but with constant reassurance from Lt. Sharples, I was able to pick up my medical records.

Mission #1 accomplished! I'm sure that's what went through Lt. Sharples's head at that time.

When I picked up my records, they handed me a plastic card. Immediately I thought, *This is my admittance card. She tricked me!*

I turned to Lt. Sharples and asked, real quick; "What's this for?"

She answered, as quickly as I asked, "That's just a card they give everyone so you can show you picked up your records. I have one, too. Here, let me show you."

She whipped her little white card with blue lettering out of her wallet.

I took hers and compared it to mine. They looked the same. Both read MEDICAL SERVICE in big blue letters across the top and then the name and social security number of the card owner.

Okay, I thought. *Lt. Sharples has one and she's not locked up. I guess this isn't my ticket to the nut house. Maybe Lt. Sharples is telling me the truth. I haven't proven her wrong yet and we spent many hours together today.*

I put my medical service card in my wallet with my ID card and we moved down the hallway, back past the cafeteria, down to the stairwell at the end of the hallway across from the flower shop. This was it now. It was 2:30 in the afternoon. I felt as if we had been through months of work just to get to this point in time. We were just five flights away from the doctor's office.

We walked through the door leading to the stairwell. "Are we going to the doctor now?" I asked, as we started climbing the steps.

"Yes, we're going to the doctor's. It's up on the sixth floor. It's better to take the steps than the elevator."

The elevator was just a few feet away from the steps. I was glad we were taking the steps, though; It took longer than the elevator. I started to think as we started our climb. Lt. Sharples was talking the whole way up: "Wow, this climb will get you in shape for P.T., Ranaghan. I'm tired already and we're only halfway there."

It was between the fourth and the fifth floor that I said to Lt. Sharples one of the few sentences I had uttered that morning that was not spoken out of fear, but sincere gratitude. It came straight from my heart to my mouth. I said, "You know, Lt. Sharples, I don't like what's happening to me right now. I don't like where you are taking me, but I have a feeling I will thank you for the rest of my life."

Lt. Sharples didn't say anything for a few seconds. Then she said, "We'll see, Ranaghan. We'll see."

Seven
Meeting with the Doctor

We sat in the waiting room for at least 20 minutes before the man with the white jacket, the silver-framed glasses, the grayish white balding hair, and the strong confident voice entered. He approached where Lt. Sharples and I were sitting, in two seats just in front of the receptionist's desk where we had signed in. We talked a lot while we were waiting for the doctor; I kept looking over at the receptionist to make sure she wasn't purposely trying to overhear our conversation. I was sure she was listening and taking notes too. *Maybe the doctor put her there and told her to listen and take notes on what I was saying?* I thought.

Most of our conversation was about things from the past, unpleasant memories of my family and recollections of why I had joined the military. I had never spoken so much about my family before. Now it was all that I spoke about. Lt. Sharples was listening, never seeming to grow tired of my incessant rambling and questioning. And she always responded to me as if I were a normal person. I really didn't feel very normal, but I was very comfortable now with Lt. Sharples.

Once in a while she'd share something about her family with me. She told me about her grandfather who built a chin-up bar in their house. He'd take his kids and have them grasp the bars with their hands and then he'd let them go, leaving them hanging there. I guess it was supposed to make them strong. I must have been talking about something that reminded her of that. She said they had to either hang on, hold themselves up and grow strong or fall hard in a heap on the ground.

"Ranaghan. You are Ranaghan, aren't you?" a man in a white jacket inquired.

"Yes."

"Would you like to follow me and come into my office? The lieutenant can wait right here. She'll be here when you come out." Turning to Lt. Sharples he said, "You can wait right here. Okay, Lieutenant?"

"Yes, sir."

I remembered the last time I had gone into an office without Lt. Sharples and I hadn't liked it much, so I was a little hesitant. Lt. Sharples assured me she'd be there when I finished, so I went ahead in.

Dr. Cambridge was straightforward with me and he intimidated me in very much the same way Sgt. Houzer did. But there was something different about Dr. Cambridge. He seemed a little sharper and a lot more professional. Maybe I only thought that because he wore a white jacket and had Dr. in front of his name.

"So why are you here? Why have you been brought to see me?"

I gave a sheepish smile and shrugged my shoulders. He repeated the question. I answered, "I'm an alcoholic."

That was the only answer I could come up with, even though I felt my being an alcoholic did not explain the bizarre experiences I'd been having. I could not connect my alcoholism with what felt like my impending insanity. It felt strange, like a lie, to be calling myself an alcoholic, especially since I couldn't admit it when I was at a meeting of Alcoholics Anonymous. I wasn't comfortable with it and I didn't believe it was an adequate explanation for what was going on in my life at that time. When I thought of the word "alcoholic" I thought of a falling-down drunk, not of someone whose distorted view of reality remained whether they were drunk or dry. How nice it would have been if alcohol was really the problem; then I could quit drinking and the problem would be over. How nice that would have been.

"When is the last time you had a drink?" the doctor asked briskly.

"Eight months ago. I had champagne and beer on my graduation from college—lots of it. That night I lay on a mattress on the floor in my room and cried hysterically because I would be leaving college the next morning and I didn't want to. I was so alone. My friends couldn't understand why I was in such an inconsolable state and I couldn't explain to them what was wrong because I hardly knew myself."

"So how is it you think you're an alcoholic, when you haven't had a drink in eight months?"

"Well, in AA I hear them saying things like 'It's not how much you drink or when you drink. It's what the drink does to the person.' And I had a bit of trouble when I drank alcohol."

"So what are you doing here today?"

While Dr. Cambridge questioned me he was also reading the write-up Sgt. Houzer had done on me. He then decided to read it aloud:

REASON FOR REQUEST:

In Germany five weeks. Onset of present disturbance apparently insidious. Seems to have some questions about her identity, wondering if something is wrong with her. Been attending AA (drinking since age 14 but abuse is unclear). When AA members said they were "sick" she left the meetings (in alarm). Began to feel various experiences (prosaic on the surface) were omens. On 12 Feb 87 had a strange, dissociated experience as if possessed by God.

PROVISIONAL DIAGNOSIS:

Possibly early schizophreniform disorder: possible mixed personality disorder, borderline with schizotypal and histrionic features.

CONSULTATION REPORT:

During interview soldier reported being possessed by God, having difficulty concentrating, movement being impaired as evidenced by soldier sitting in a corner of her room unable to move. Bill Joel tape is constantly played by the soldier in her room. Frequent perplexity and a feeling of confusion are present as evidenced by the way she responds to questions. Please evaluate.

Sgt. George Houzer, 91G20
FKT, Community Counseling Center

While Dr. Cambridge was reading the write-up I thought, *That couldn't be me he's talking about! That describes a crazy, sick individual, not me. I never said that. I can't be that insane! What if I am! Is that really me? Am I that bad? What's wrong with me? NO! NO! NO! WHAT IS GOING ON!*
Dr. Cambridge was very quick and very wise. He

61

sensed my fear immediately. If I wasn't answering him straightforwardly, if I beat around the bush in any way, he caught me at it and confronted me. He instantly picked up on my insecurities. My hiding was all over. What you saw was what you got. I was still trying to be evasive, but it was not working with the doctor. It hadn't worked with Sgt. Houzer either. This left me with a gut full of fear. And fear was the very thing that drove me to break down. Fear is the one word I could use 10,000 times over again and still it would not be enough times to emphasize how I felt to be living in it.

The interviews seemed more intimidating to me than helpful. Nothing connected. Nothing made sense. And no one, except Lt. Sharples, was on my side. At least I did have one person. . . .

I came out of Dr. Cambridge's office only about 15 minutes after I went in. Lt. Sharples was gone. My heart leaped when I saw the empty chair. My eyes searched the entire waiting area room and I yelled to the receptionist, "Where'd she go?"

The receptionist was calm. She smiled and said, "She just went downstairs. She'll be right back."

I sat down in the same seat I had been sitting in, next to Lt. Sharples, who wasn't there, and I waited what seemed like a lifetime, but was only 30 seconds. I started getting antsy. I was also very hungry. It was late in the afternoon and I hadn't eaten anything since breakfast the day before.

I stood up and timidly walked toward the door. I thought maybe the receptionist would not let me leave by myself because she didn't know if I'd come back, but she didn't say a word, so I managed to walk out the door and take myself down to the first floor to find the little shoppette we passed earlier so I could grab a big fat chocolate bar. I ate half of it by the time I got back to my seat in the waiting room. Lt. Sharples wasn't back yet. *Where had she gone? Had she left for good?* I started to get butterflies in my stomach. I was about to stand up and ask the receptionist where exactly Lt. Sharples had gone when she came walking through the door. She had brought me a big chocolate donut from the donut shop downstairs. First I felt relieved that she had returned. Then I felt guilty because I didn't think to buy her a chocolate bar. I asked her if she wanted a bite of mine.

"No, thanks."

"Well, why not?"

"Because I just had a donut."

"Oh, well—I feel funny eating by myself. You sure you don't want a bite?"

"No thanks, Ranaghan. I'm full."

She smiled one of those smiles that spread across her entire face, all the way to her ears, and made her eyes light up. Lt. Sharples was happy and secure with herself, from the inside out, not the outside in.

Lt. Sharples and I sat for about another forty-five minutes before Dr. Cambridge called us both back into his office. Now we were going to have a threesome, but it seemed more like a twosome with a onesome as a listener. Dr. Cambridge directed all his questioning at me, and Lt. Sharples sat and listened intently. She had a serious, thoughtful look on her face as she observed the conversation going back and forth between myself and Dr. Cambridge.

"What do you think is the worst possible thing you could ever possibly do, something that would be absolutely unforgivable?"

I had to think for a minute. I wasn't really thinking. I knew the answer immediately, but I was thinking about whether I should be honest or not. I believed at that time that the worst possible thing I could ever find out about myself would be that I was a lesbian. I really didn't know for sure whether I was or not, but I thought I might be and it wasn't okay. It was okay for others to be gay, but it wasn't okay for *me* to be gay. It was this hidden fear that popped into my mind when Dr. Cambridge asked me about this "unforgivable thing." But I could never say that. I'd be giving myself away. I never expressed my greatest fear, which is why it remained my greatest fear. In this situation I could never express it because maybe Dr. Cambridge would use one of his psychological tricks and turn it into something more than it was. In other words he would somehow magically turn my fear into a reality and I would instantly become that which I feared most.

So instead of telling him that being a lesbian seemed most frightening and unforgivable to me, I told him the second thought which popped into my mind: "I would never want to sleep with a married man." Again, my greatest fear had to do with sexuality in some way. I'd had many crushes on different married men. It seemed like all the men I ever liked were married, or taken, or fifty years old. But I had tremendous guilt built up inside of me just for thinking how nice it would be. How strange it was that fears around sexual issues would be so prominent when clearly there were more immediate issues I might have been most fearful of, such as the loss of my own sanity.

I made an observation about Hemingway in the session. Dr. Cambridge asked me if I wanted to commit suicide. I said no, but I brought up some friends of mine from American Literature who had committed suicide. I mentioned them because I believed I thought the same way they thought. I mentioned Zelda, too. I once wrote a short story about a day I spent on the corner of Forty-second Street selling ices. I had named myself Zelda in the story and although my story talked about the frustration of being a street vendor, I believed inside that I was Zelda and I was going to wind up institutionalized one day, being studied under a glass by some sophisticated doctors who spoke a language of their own.

Zelda (F. Scott Fitzgerald's wife) went insane and was a mental patient in a psychiatric ward at the end of her life, and Hemingway committed suicide. I had read their biographies. Reading was very dangerous for me because I would take on the identity of the characters in the book for a short while. I faked insanity—at least I thought I was faking it—and then the day came when I was convinced I wasn't faking anymore.

When the doctor asked me about suicide, I immediately thought of these writers. I had some strong ideas about what life was about from all the reading I had done as an English major. Most of the time I understood only bits and pieces of writings because I never was much for putting a whole book together. But I would always remember the parts about the darker side of the mind.

"No, I don't want to commit suicide."

Lt. Sharples was listening intently.

"So what was your breaking point? What was the straw that broke the camel's back? What do you remember happening to you that made you feel you needed help? What led up to you crawling up in a ball in the corner of your room?"

I had to think for a minute. My mind was jam-packed with events that had made me feel unbearably uncomfortable, especially recent ones which occurred in the military. Ever since I joined the army I had been terribly conscious of being uncomfortable with authority and it seemed that too many people had the right to tell me what to do, and that many of them worked on the fear tactic rather than the mutual respect tactic.

After running a few episodes through my head, I answered: "Well, when I first got to my unit, they put me in a room with a sergeant and the sergeant didn't want me in her room. She stood there screaming when she came in and found me sitting in her chair with my luggage scattered in front of me on her floor. She started yelling about how I could have been a thief or something and how dare they let me in her room. I felt like I was not wanted and I was scared and I started to cry uncontrollably. I just wanted to be left alone. I wanted to know how I got there, why I was there, and how I was going to survive in the army, in this unit, for two and a half years. I didn't know what to do, I didn't know a soul and I wanted to pretend none of this had happened, that the army was just a bad dream, and I would wake up and I would be home, not in the army."

"How did you feel when the sergeant was standing there yelling at you while you were sitting right there?"

"Well, I can really understand how she felt. She had her own room and she was a sergeant and I just showed up and took over her space. I can understand how she felt."

"Ah, come on, you mean to tell me you didn't feel angry or hurt that someone was standing there screaming at you with no consideration of who you are or how you felt?"

"I wasn't angry. I understand how she felt. She had a right to feel that way. I invaded her space."

Dr. Cambridge glanced over at Lt. Sharples and then they both looked at me. I didn't understand what it was that I was missing. I felt that they knew something that I didn't, but what exactly was it?

The day the sergeant had screamed about me being in her room was a breaking point. I knew that night when I rested my head on the pillow that I wasn't going to make it. I couldn't possibly go on like this. I would either have to go insane or die because I had no coping mechanisms left. I could no longer hide my fear and insecurity. It showed on my face as clear as a huge black freckle. It showed in my reactions, and it showed in my eyes. If you took even a glance into my eyes they would communicate: RUN! RUN! RUN! BUT WHERE! BUT WHERE! BUT WHERE!

"So how can I be sure that you don't have suicidal intentions that you aren't speaking of?"

"I don't want to die. I just want to know what's wrong with me. If I wanted to commit suicide I'd have done that instead of crawling up in a ball in the corner of my room. I want to live."

"Have you ever attempted suicide?"

I had to lie now because if I admitted that I had then he surely would lock me up in an asylum. At the moment that was my biggest fear. If Dr. Cambridge suspected that I was capable, in any way, of harming myself, he was going to admit me. I had made a feeble attempt at suicide when I was drunk one night in college, but I rationalized that that didn't count because I hadn't wound up in the hospital. The truth was that I often thought of suicide when I drank and even sometimes when I sobered up. When you feel hopeless and depressed, suicide seems like an easy way out.

"No, I never attempted suicide."

"Have you ever thought about suicide?"

"No, I never thought about it."

67

"Well, what do you think about when you get so depressed?"

"I think about how joining the military was the biggest mistake of my life."

"So do you want to get out of the military?"

"No. No, I don't want to get out of the army. I think I"ll be fine if I can just go back to work."

"Well, how am I supposed to be convinced that if you leave here today you won't commit suicide? Otherwise I'm going to have to admit you to the ward down the hall. That's what you don't want, isn't it? You are afraid of getting locked up in the psychiatric ward."

"I don't need to be in the hospital! I am fine. I will not commit suicide. I don't want to die."

"What are you going to do for the weekend? Do you have friends you are going to spend the weekend with, or are you going to be alone?"

"I have friends from AA and I'll spend the weekend with them. I won't be alone."

"You just don't want to be locked up, isn't that it?"

"Why would I want to be locked up when I don't need to be?"

"What is it about a psychiatric ward that you are afraid of? Are you afraid of what people would think of you if they found out you were there? You are afraid of the stigma attached to being on a psych ward, aren't you?"

"I don't need to be in there. I will be with my friends all weekend."

"So if I let you go home for the weekend and you make an appointment to come back and see me on Tuesday, you are not going to do anything rash? This is a three-day weekend, and I can make an appointment for you to come back and see me on Tuesday morning. Do you think you can hang in there until Tuesday?"

"Yes, I think I'll be fine. I'll just go to a lot of meetings and spend my time with people from the program.

"Okay. I'm going to let you go. You're on your honor. And Tuesday morning you will be back for another appointment, at 9:30 A.M. We'll see how the weekend goes and then we'll take it from there. How does that sound?"

"That's fine with me."

"Lt. Sharples, does that sound reasonable to you?"

"Yes, sir. That's okay with me."

Lt. Sharples and I left the office after we had all agreed on the compromise. I wondered to myself how Dr. Cambridge knew of my fear of the psych ward. That was the very thing that had kept me from asking for help earlier. That was the trick I thought the military was playing on me, trying to get me locked on a ward for the mentally disturbed. When I was growing up I became angry and rebellious at times, screaming my head off behind the bathroom door until my mother couldn't take it anymore. Then she would threaten to call the police or the board of child welfare so they would come and take me away in a straitjacket. I was crazy, she said. While I screamed, she would pretend to be calling someone on the telephone to come and take me away. But now I was safe. I was leaving the hospital with Lt. Sharples and I hadn't been committed.

I looked forward to Tuesday. I felt, "Well, this is it. Tuesday Dr. Cambridge will have the answers to all my problems and he will reveal them to me. There is hope!" I smiled and felt safe because Lt. Sharples had been right again. I would not be left to rot on what I called, at that time, the nut ward.

After just one day with Lt. Sharples, I found it terrifying and difficult to leave her side once we returned to our unit. I followed her down to the basement. She was going to conduct business unrelated to me. She had to spell it out to me: "Okay, Ranaghan. We're done for today. You can go upstairs to your room. I'll see you Tuesday at work. Bye-bye." But I didn't want to leave her side. I felt physically attached to her and I was tearing myself in half, ripping myself apart, destroying my body, when I tried to walk away from her. It hurt so bad. But I had to do it, no matter how much pain it caused me. I was not at the point where I could articulate to Lt. Sharples how I felt and even if I could, I was too ashamed of how I felt. My feelings had to be kept secret, I thought, because they were wrong. They were disastrous and "unforgivable."

If I had had the wisdom and insight gained only through years of internal torture, hospitalizations, suicide attempts, and therapy, I might have answered differently Dr. Cambridge's question about the most unforgivable act. I might have told him the most unforgivable thing I could ever possibly do would be to have a child and abandon it.

Eight
The Day They Locked Me Up

Tuesday morning arrived. I had lived the weekend barely making it from one hour to the next. It wasn't as easy as I thought it would be. I was losing my mind, and it didn't matter where I was or who I was with. Losing your mind is a process of mental solitary confinement where you believe that absolutely no one, including yourself, has any idea what is going on within you, that no one has ever felt the way you feel right now. They couldn't possibly have felt this way and survived. I wrote the following letter and read it at an AA meeting on Sunday night over that weekend. It was the first time I ever opened up my mouth at a meeting:

I keep trying to figure out when the game is going to end. When is everyone going to tear off their costumes and peel off their masks, and let me know who they really are. When are the actors going to step out of the play and back into reality, or is the play reality for them?

Who are you people, really? Why do you insist on tricking me? I must know when this is going to end. How long do I have to go on like this, wondering about everything, never knowing what's going on around me. I can't remember from one minute to the next. I have a dreadful fear that admitting I'm an alcoholic is not going to solve my problems. Once I admit this, I've only stepped through the first door, and then there's millions of other doors waiting for me. What in the name of God am I going to discover about myself? Am I insane? Schizo? Am I going to wind up in the psych ward of some mental institution? Is that my fate? Am I living a self-fulfilling prophecy?

I feel as if I have been sitting in AA meetings absorbing all the conversation, but never contributing because to contribute is to admit, and once you admit, there's no turning back. And I'm scared that if the rest of my life is going to be anything like this past month has been, then it really isn't worth living.

I am highly suspicious of anyone who cares about me. I have to wonder what their ulterior motive might be. Are they trying to portray me as the sick little runt, just so that they don't have to look so sick themselves? I haven't done a lousy thing for any of you, for instance. So why do you want to do something for me?

Why are my mood swings so severe? How long am I going to be placed at the top of the cliff and then dropped off, time and time again? When will God provide a way for me to escape from this inner turmoil, this mental torture?

I only had two-and-one-half hours to live through before my appointment with Dr. Cambridge. How would I manage two and one-half hours in the office with people around me, I anxiously wondered. And what if the telephone rang? I'd probably have to answer it, and I don't like answering with that line we have to give: "HHD, 596th Military Police Battalion, PFC Ranaghan speaking, may I help you Sir, Ma'am?" And then they'd ask me something and I wouldn't know the answer. I was lucky to know my own name. What if I had to go upstairs and use the copy machine? There was a sign above the copy machine which said USE OF COPY MACHINE MUST BE APPROVED BY MSG ABCOX. The last time I had used the machine I didn't have the courage to ask him if I could use it. I had just gone ahead and used it and prayed he wouldn't say anything to me. He noticed, though, and he bawled me out right there in front of everyone.

What if they ask me to bring a message to someone and I forget the message? I'm not doing too well at remembering things.

I sat in the office in the seat that visitors sit in. Sgt. Marx asked me to do something very simple, put some papers in chronological order. I sat there for the two and one-half hours and felt myself left alone and on the verge of tears. But after a while, I didn't have the energy for tears. I was too depressed. I was just shuffling papers around on my lap. They meant nothing to me. I didn't care what they were. I didn't care if I screwed them up. I didn't care that I was accomplishing nothing. The haunting thoughts, which had been racing through my head a little earlier, were dissolving. My mind was settling, giving in and giving up. I was crumbling into submission. Even the racing, confusing fears didn't seem to matter. The fear of my thoughts was leaving. I didn't care enough to be afraid anymore. I found myself whining one sentence inside: "Someone please help me. Someone, PLEASE help me!" And hearing the plea the same whiner answered: "No one can help you. No one can help you. It doesn't matter. Nothing matters. IT JUST DOESN'T MATTER."

I didn't care that I looked depressed. I didn't care if people came into the office and wondered what was wrong with the girl sitting on the chair in the corner. I just couldn't care anymore. The outside no longer mattered.

I walked myself to the hospital that morning. I remembered the way. I took the stairs up to the sixth floor because the stairs reminded me of Lt. Sharples and our conversation on the way up the stairs a few days earlier. I signed in at the receptionist's desk and I took the same seat I sat in on the Friday before when Lt. Sharples was with me. Dr. Cambridge came into the receptionist area and called for me five minutes after I arrived.

Dr. Cambridge had three chairs in his office, set up in the same way they were the first time I was there. His office was set up so that when he swiveled around from writing at his desk the three chairs were in a circle. When he was writing at his desk, I could see only the right side of his body and face. Looking at his profile gave me a sense that my presence in his office was not that important and that he would deal with me at his convenience. At the same time I almost felt claustrophobic in the room with him. His office was so small that when he was facing me, his knees were only inches from mine.

"How was your weekend?" he asked.

"Fine."

"No major catastrophes, huh?"

"No."

He was talking quickly, starting the next question just about the same time I was getting around to answering the first question.

Soon things got serious and I reverted to a defensive posture.

"Why are you here?" he asked.

"Because I have an appointment."

"You could have forgotten about it if you wanted to. Why did you show up?"

"When you have an appointment it's common courtesy to show up."

"So that's the only reason why you're here, because you have an appointment and you feel obligated to be courteous to me?"

"No. I'm here because I hate my job too."

"Do you want to get out of the army?"

I really didn't want to get out of the army, not because I was discovering it to be a wonderful organization, tailormade to meet my needs and make use of my undiscovered talents, but because I would be too ashamed to go home a reject, a failure, the one who couldn't even make it in the army. I was willing to suffer more in order to keep my image in proper shape. The rest of the world would never know that I couldn't manage to turn every impulsive move I made into a miraculous victory. So I would rather die than get out of the army before my time was up. People would ask me what was wrong if I got out now. "I thought you enlisted for three years," they'd say. "Oh, yes, but I was diagnosed a manic-depressive-schizophrenic-personality-disordered alcoholic so I got a psychiatric discharge." No way!! I'd rather go insane!

I answered Dr. Cambridge: "I don't know. I'm not happy. Something's wrong with me. I can't go back to work, though. I really hate it there. The people there are trying to drive me crazy. They are intentionally trying to drive me nuts. I hate those people. They are so manipulative. Sick individuals."

"It sounds like you think the world is out to get you. Give me some examples. You need to show where you have been manipulated. You don't have any evidence. You make statements, but you present no situations in which you have actually been manipulated. This leads me to believe you have a paranoia disorder, and no one is manipulating you. You only imagine they are."

"I can't explain it," I went on, "because when I explain it, it sounds so bizarre and crazy, but believe me these army people are something else. All of them think they can tell me what to do and get away with it. They are trying to control me."

I tried to explain to Dr. Cambridge about the ser-

75

geant who picked at me and said "A nice little Irish girl. I like nice little Irish girls. A few weeks in this place and you'll be screwing every guy in the unit."

And I tried to explain about my roommate who badgered me constantly because I didn't do things right, because I was always forgetting something, like my key for example. One time I went down the hall to take a shower and I forgot my key and when I came back, she had locked me out and I had to go walking around the barracks in my pajamas, looking for her. Then I had to go around to the Battalion Commander's office at the other end of the hall because that's where she usually was. When I found her she laughed at me and said: "That will teach you not to forget your key. Your key is like your ID card. You don't go anywhere without it. And don't go walking off to the shower leaving my door open ever again."

Dr. Cambridge was about to let me go. We weren't getting very far in our conversation. I felt scared to walk out of his office. What would I do then? Where would I go? *Who's going to help me? I can't go back to work. I'd rather crawl up in a ball and die.*

The insecurity wasn't so easy to hide. Dr. Cambridge looked at me and said, "Okay, you can go back to work now."

"I can't go back to work. I hate my job."

"Well, in the army you have two choices. Either you go to work or you go into the hospital."

"Well, I'll go back to work then."

"Well, I just took your choices away. You're going into the hospital."

Suddenly I got an overwhelming burst of energy and a newfound knowledge that there was absolutely nothing wrong with me, that I was as fine as anyone else around. I felt compelled to explain to the doctor just how fine I was and how big a mistake this whole thing was. What a terrible mistake to put such a healthy person such as myself into a nut ward. I told him: "That would only worsen the situation. I am not crazy! I have no business on the psych ward, the dumping grounds for the weirdos of society."

He paid as much attention to me as he would to a harmless fly on the wall in the next room. He continued writing up his paper work with his back to me, not even swiveling around to listen.

"I am ordering you into the hospital. This is a direct order."

"I have never been in the hospital overnight. I am very healthy, you see. You just don't seem to understand. . . ."

I resisted with my words, but the attempt was weak and I hadn't won a battle with this man yet. I knew in my heart my life was in this man's hands and I was giving up on trying to work it my way. I was drifting into submission, slowly, but definitely. I was on my way. He was determined to hospitalize me, and he was untouched by anything I had to say. I wanted to get on my hands and knees and beg him not to do this to me, but I didn't have the faith to think that that would work either. That would only reassure him about his decision.

He walked out of the office first. I had trouble getting myself up out of the chair. My fate was closing in on me. He said if I didn't get up and walk down the hall to the psych ward, then he'd get them to come and pick me up, literally. I was shaking like a leaf hanging off its branch, about to fall off with just the slightest breeze. I followed, scared out of my mind, too afraid to rebel. I didn't want them to put me in a straitjacket. I knew those things happened. I remembered my mother's shrieks from years ago when I was throwing a temper tantrum. She would scream to me as I locked myself behind the bathroom door; "I'm calling the police! They'll come and take you away in a straitjacket! That's where you belong, in the back of a paddy wagon headed to the nut house!" Then she would pretend she was dialing and she'd speak into the phone as if the police were on the other end. The terror and helplessness were unbearable then, just exactly as they were now.

I followed Dr. Cambridge down the hall, the tears streaming down my face. I kept asking him questions, but he never came out with a straight answer. I mustered the strength to ask him how long I would be locked up. "It depends," he answered. "If you don't improve we'll have to medevac you back to Washington, D.C., to the major hospital for further evaluation."

Oh God, I thought. *Please don't let that happen to me!! They'd all know!! Maybe they'd lock me up for good! What if I never get out? What if I'm schizophrenic? I know there's something wrong with me! There always has been! I was a strange insane kid and I grew up to be a strange insane adult. There's no way of changing that. My history shows total insane behavior from my early days when I used to torture my mother with my relentless screaming, until now, at the age of 22, when I crawled up in a ball in the corner of my barracks room. My record, if they ever referred to anyone from my past, would surely certify me as mentally insane and incapable of adapting to any normal way of living and this is grounds for lifelong institutionalization.*

Nine
Psychiatric Intake

Consultation Report

Picture is of a bizarre dissociative state of events being interpreted by patient as having an omen-significance (an invasion of meaningfulness from the unconscious) with interpretation by patient of possible "Possession by God" (not the devil). But doubts and anxiety as to what is altering consciousness.

Appears ±normal. But has an aloof, guarded evasiveness as if wary, cautious, afraid of what is happening to her from within and how it will be interpreted by outsiders; alert, oriented X3, cooperative, memory intact, denies hallucinations; paranoia (e.g., some omen-like references, feelings of being mildly persecuted, possible thought-reading, etc.) is present in traces.

*Possible Schizophreniform Disorder
Schizotypal Personality Disorder
*Admit to Inpatient Services
Signed: <u>Dr. Cambridge</u>

The intake was difficult. I was a hysterical patient, very unhappy about my involuntary admission onto the psychiatric ward. I was told by the nurse to put on my pajamas and I refused. After refusing for a long period, I was told, "Put the pajamas on or we will strap you down and put them on for you." Hearing this, I locked myself in the bathroom, my childhood reprieve from conflict and abuse. I gripped the handle of the window and begged God for mercy and freedom from this insane asylum. I cried so hard I had a massive headache, the hiccups, and I couldn't breathe through my nose. The humiliation, to think these people believed I was a nutcase and the fear, because I believed it myself!

I slid my hands from the window handle down the wall in the bathroom, desperately clinging, yet knowing there was nothing to cling to on the slippery tiles. I slid down slowly until I crumpled in a heap on the cold bathroom floor, where I sat, closer to the pajamas which were now on the floor next to me. I was scared again, too scared not to do what I was told. It was reminiscent of the scenes in my childhood when I was forced by fear to beg my mother for mercy from behind the door I had my full body weight up against. In a few situations, I did have to submit and beg for forgiveness for pushing my mother over the edge.

But my verbal pleas were useless because the damage had already been done and I was going to get what was waiting for me on the other side of the door, whether that be confinement to the apartment for the next few days, or a good spanking on my bare ass. The bare ass spankings were shame inducing because I had to go through the humiliation of someone ripping my pants off in such a physically aggressive way, and then having my bare skin smacked until it was beet red. It was like she couldn't stop once she started. The smacks got harder and harder and then my entire body, head to toe, were the target for the once smacks but now wallops and punches. It was never the pain of being hit that bothered me so much. It was the humiliation and shame of having my private areas exposed and touched. Then I would be left alone, on the bed, to pull my pants up and pull myself together with the last words, "That's what you get, you little bastard" ringing in my ears.

I imagined the staff tying me up and undressing me to put me in the pajamas, pulling my pants off me, my underwear sliding down, my body exposed, them unbuttoning my shirt and raising my body to pull the tee shirt over my head and then putting my arms through the pajama shirt and buttoning it up the front, seeing my breasts and touching my skin all the while. This made me cringe from the inside.

I heard a woman's voice right outside the bathroom door. She was singing loudly, nothing that made any sense, and I heard the nurse come by and say, "Hishu. Go to your room." Hishu must have been the Korean woman, the one I saw when I first walked onto the ward. She was swinging her arms around and turning herself, as if dancing with a partner, around and around. The sight of her stirred up tremendous anxiety. Now hearing her outside the door made me feel even worse about putting the pajamas on. It also made me do it because I didn't want to be like Hishu. If I acted crazy, they might drug me up like they did to Hishu! I slowly took my army fatigues off and slid the pajama pants on, ever so conscious of every inch of the blue cloth that crept up my legs. The same with the shirt. It felt horrible for the pajamas to be touching my skin . . . total defeat . . . humiliation . . . being told to put on a pair of hospital pajamas, because I was no longer a human being with the ability or the freedom to decide for myself what was good for me. Now I was nothing more than a victim of mental and spiritual torture.

Putting the pajamas on was the hardest part because it signified the reality of admission. Everyone else on the

81

ward had them on and now I was one of them. It was official now. I wore the uniform.

The nurse took my army clothes away and asked me if I had any money or my identification card. I had my wallet in my hand and my dog tags still around my neck. I had walked into the room next to the nurse's station after I put my pajamas on. I darted from the bathroom to my sleeping room since I had already been told I would be in the room right next to the nurse's station because I was on 24-hour watch. "They're even going to watch me sleep," I muttered to myself. I was sitting on the stripped mattress in my room, which had one other empty bed in it, when a heavy-set social worker came in and asked for my identification card. I resisted giving it to her. She needed some information from it for the records and I refused to give it to her. I was hysterical, crying and wheezing and losing my breath because all these people were invading me, stripping me of my most basic freedoms which I took for granted on a regular basis. I had never thought of choosing which clothes I wanted to wear in the morning as a freedom. I never thought of going to work as a freedom. I hadn't thought of being left alone as a freedom. I had taken the freedom in my life for granted!!

I finally handed over the ID card after holding onto it like it was my very precious gift. I never realized how important an ID card could be! When I handed it over, my hand reaching out and shaking, my fear turned into anger. Next came the dog tags which hung around my neck. I hated wearing dog tags every day, but now it seemed important that I be allowed to keep them on me. I screamed, "WHY DO I HAVE TO HAND OVER MY DOG TAGS? THEY ARE MINE! MINE! MINE! MINE!"

"We don't allow the patients to hold on to anything in the hospital. You will get them back, but right now we need everything from you. We will put your stuff in a safety vault and you will get them back when you leave."

The social worker was very polite. *Why shouldn't she be?* I thought. *It wasn't her ass that was tossed in the nut house. She was on the incarceration committee!*

My first meal on the psychiatric ward was lunch. I arrived on the ward at about 10:00 A.M. and lunch came up at 11:30 A.M. I wasn't hungry when the trays were brought up from the cafeteria. I was still crying and very unaware of anything but my whereabouts and the need to get out. I could not have eaten my meal in peace even if I had wanted to. The same evil-looking nurse, who threatened to tie me down to the bed if I didn't put the pajamas on, was hot on my tail. I only ate because I was afraid not to. As I swallowed my fried chicken like a vicious wild animal who was eating for the first time in months, she sat directly across from me and continued to ask me questions, the same ones I'd been asked five times already by five different staff members: Name? Denise Ranaghan. Social Security Number? 095-95-8765. Unit? 596th MP Bn. Deros date (date of departure)? July 30, 1989. Hobbies? None. I answered the questions with a mouth full of food, not caring what hung out of my mouth. I wanted to shove the chicken in her face, but some voice inside of me warned me: "Eat, because if you don't they will write you up and use it as an excuse to give you some medication; do not physically harm anyone because they will strap you to the bed; answer all questions the same or they will diagnose you schizophrenic." The temptation to screw everything up was so overwhelming, but the fear of what might happen to me if I played the wise-ass overpowered me.

I enjoyed my dessert more than the chicken. It was three chocolate chip cookies and some kind of fruit cake.

Hishu had been by and tried to steal my cookies. She was out of it, drugged up, and made not a word of sense. I was pretty firm in telling her to get her hands off my plate. She mumbled something in her foreign language and skipped off hastily down the hall to pester someone else. Hishu scared me to death. I thought for sure I would catch whatever disease she had if I was stuck in this nut house for too long.

Hishu's teeth were brown and crusty, and every time she opened her mouth to mumble, shout or sing, she's spit all over you. I only ate the two cookies underneath the top one because I never knew what kind of germs she was spreading. I didn't want the fruit cake, but I was too annoyed with Hishu for pestering me so I didn't offer it to her. I threw it out. At first Hishu reminded me of an untrained dog at meal times, but once I was up there for a while, I became immune to her bad habits. She wasn't more than five feet tall, with a skinny, emaciated body, shoulder-length jet black hair, dark Korean eyes, and a dark complexion. I couldn't help but wonder what Hishu was like without the drugs she was on. *But for the grace of God there go I,* I thought. Then I thought, *Oh God, there go I if I don't do everything right. If they did it to her they could do it to me!*

After lunch I had one more interview with a member of the staff and was asked the same questions.

"Name?"

"I told the others my name about twenty times already! What the hell are you asking me again for? Go get the notes from your friends!"

"Rank?"

"Colonel."

"Unit?"

"Military Police."

84

"Which Military Police?"

"The ones down the block!"

"Social Security Number?"

"000-00-0000."

"Deros date?"

"Yesterday."

"Hobbies?"

"Writing. I love to write."

"Write what?"

"Words! Lousy, fuckin' words!"

"You seem to be very uncooperative? Are you irritated?"

"No. It's my natural disposition. It interferes at the most inopportune moments of my life."

After that interview, which was the last required one for the intake, I was left alone. I was told not to be in my room during the day. I could only be in the TV room or at the end of the hall where the ping pong table and the foosball table was. And I was on 24-hour watch.

I found my way to the smoky TV room directly across the hall from the nurse's station. A bunch of guys were in there. They looked very relaxed and laid back, just smoking their cigarettes and staring at the TV screen. I sat in an empty lounge chair. I looked toward the TV and my stomach began to jump around. I tried to hold back the tears, but they burst out and I was hysterical again, hysterical for the rest of the afternoon.

I wondered about my family. My friends: *Where is everybody? I have nobody. I am sitting on the psychiatric ward of a hospital in Germany and nobody even knows me. Those who do know me don't know I'm here. What would my family think if they ever did know? Or my friends from college. This is where I wound up after all my hard work and years of struggling to keep up with every-*

one else. I am alone. No one can ever comprehend this experience. No one is over here to protect me. No one will stand up for me. No one will listen to me. It's just me now. I am lost, so lost, lost, confused and insane. I have never been so alone in my life. I'm scared. God, are you there? You must be. Somebody has to be listening to me. Where is my hope? Where is my faith that I never had? I never needed you so much before, God. Are you laughing at me? I wonder if there is a God? Are you real, God? Are you really running this whole show? I've never seen you. Why would you want me in a place like this? No human can help me right now. I am in this alone. No one is in sight. I'm sure you know that. It's not like I can tell you anything that you don't already know. If you're up there, God, I want you to know, it's you and me all the way on this one. If you're not up there, then I would like to make believe you are for a while because if you are not real, I'm screwed. It's all over. Ain't no one else involved in this one. It's between you and me, Lord, and I beg of you to help me. Maybe I am wrong for ignoring you for so long in my life, for doubting your existence, for living a life of self-will, a life in ignorance of you, a life of self-gratification and grandiosity and self-centeredness and self-denial and addictions. I don't know where I've been or where I'm going. Please help me out of this one, God. No one is here with me. No one knows what this pain is like and I cannot stand it anymore. Help me—PLEASE!

After this extended plea for help, I stopped crying for a short breath. I was still making funny sounds from all the crying, the sound that seems like a hiccup and comes from crying too hysterically for too long. I sat there in my chair until the hiccupping stopped and I calmed down. My normal breathing was returning and I felt a little relaxed. I was tired of crying and I had no more energy left.

I got up out of my chair and walked over to the barred window right next to the TV. I looked out at the white sky and then down at the hospital parking lot just below. I watched the people walking around down there, in and out of cars, through the hospital doors, around the corner. I envied them. They were free. I was locked up. I had to lean over the window sill and peek through the bars just to get a clear view of the outside world. Life looked so good for those people down there! They had the freedom to walk about, to buy a newspaper, to get into their cars. They had no restrictions, no one shoving them onto locked wards, asking them who they were, questioning their identity. *I was like that once,* I thought. I used to be able to walk around free out there, only I never really appreciated it. It was just something I did out of habit, never really thinking that some people don't have the freedom to walk around, to go to work every morning, to go to the grocery store.

Hishu walked up beside me and imitated my pose, leaning on the window sill and peeking between the bars. She yelled something in her language. It made no sense to me, but she seemed excited. She was pointing out the window and saying something. I turned to my left to look Hishu right in the eye and for that moment, I was free! It was a kind of freedom I never experienced. I was free from all the anger and all the fear which was haunting me constantly. I felt no remorse, no anger, no pain, no fear when I looked at Hishu. I was not afraid of this woman who petrified me just a short while ago, and then made me furiously angry. Now I felt we were sharing something. Hishu was quiet for a minute and she just watched out the window with me and it was okay for now. It was okay for this woman to be standing next to me on the psychiatric ward. She was harmless. My fear of catching her disease was gone. *It was okay to gaze out the window.* I didn't feel she was invading my space. I accepted her. I felt she and I were the same, two human beings placed in the same hospital at the same time, looking out the same window. I wondered if Hishu was conscious of anything. I was sure that she was aware of something for that short period of time we looked out the window together. I wonder if she felt the peace that I felt for that moment. I accepted that I'd never know, and not knowing seemed to be okay too. All I knew was I was relieved of all the pain, the mental torture, for that short moment. I had experienced peace of mind. *Was it a coincidence that it came to me right after a prayer in which I asked for help?* Did God speak to me through Hishu?

It didn't last long, but I'll never forget it. Hishu soon walked away after she reached in her pocket, pulled out a roll of candies and stretched her hand out in my direction. She muttered something. I smiled and took one. Then she peeled the rolled paper around and handed me another one, cherry. I realized there was a person in there. She was aware of something.

When Hishu walked away, I followed a few seconds later. I walked back to my chair and sat again, staring at the TV like a zombie. Whatever I had at the window was gone. I slipped back into mental despair and slowly started to cry again, working my way up to a hysterical state. I cried and cried and cried. My head was killing me. I cried for a whole afternoon. I cried every time I looked at Hishu. I cried when they wheeled the strapped-down ranting drug addict past the TV room to the isolation room. I cried when anyone walked into the TV room; I cried when anyone walked out. The people around me looked sick and they all seemed so calm about it. I couldn't understand it for the life of me. One guy tapped me on the shoulder while I was crying and said, "You'll get used to it. It's not that bad." That set me off. (I *don't* want to get used to it!) I screeched under my breath, "What a fucking nut house, man!"

Ten
On the Ward

The first night after that long day was the worst. I spent the evening dry-heaving and losing my breath from the fits of hysterics I went into over the fact that I actually could have wound up in a place like this. *What's a college graduate like me doing in a place like this? And what if I never get out?* This I asked myself, as if a college education was not only proof that I existed as a capable being, but also a seal against insanity.

When the horror and the fear dwindled, nothing replaced it. I was left empty. I had become very familiar with emptiness and fear. I was going dead inside again, just like when I crawled up in the ball in the corner of my room. I lost my ability to respond. This always seemed to happen after I spent a significant amount of time crying and kicking and screaming and not getting anywhere. My battles from within were always followed by withdrawal, submission, regression.

When my roommate from the barracks came up to visit me that night I was sitting in the single chair in the TV room, tears still streaming down my face. It wasn't too long after dinner. I was trying very hard to be quiet about my crying now because I didn't want anyone to see me. Imagine, I made it all the way to the nutcracker suite and I still cared about what people thought! I still didn't want anyone near me and I thought if I breathed too loudly, they'd shove some kind of medication down my throat, or strap me down to a bed, or lock me up in the solitary confinement cell, the one they used for all the alkys to dry out in.

As soon as Mary, my roommate from the barracks arrived, and I saw her familiar face, I clung to her as if she were my last hope. I was so happy to see a familiar, "normal" face and as soon as I saw her, my emotions shot up and my crying became screaming and screeching, and begging Mary to get me out of there. She took my hand and walked me from the TV room to my sleeping room next to the nurse's station. I sat on my bed and she pulled up a chair alongside my bed.

"Mary, you have to get me out of here! *Do something!* They think I'm crazy! I don't need to be here! All these people are insane! Please, get me out of here!"

"Denise, calm down. You'll be okay. You really will. God will take care of you. You have to believe that. You have to get strong. Don't give up now. Just believe that you will not be here long. You'll be out of here soon. Believe me!"

"I want to get out NOW. I can't take it up here! They are driving me crazy! What if they decide I really am crazy and they lock me up for good? Maybe they'll even use me as a guinea pig for experiments. You have to get me out of here! No one else can help me!"

"Denise, I can't do anything. You know that. You have to believe that this is going to make you a stronger person in the end. You won't be here forever. This is only temporary. You have to cope with it just for a little while. Believe me, you won't be here long."

"When am I going to—In the middle of my sentence I had to get off the bed and stumble to the sink in my room, where I threw up my dinner. My stomach was in knots. My physical pain was too much to ignore and I knew I'd have to calm down because my body couldn't take it anymore. I was physically weak and my body was nothing but shaky tremors.

Mary didn't stay long. Her words of wisdom helped me very little at the time, but very little was better than not at all. I didn't want her to leave. I didn't want to lose the only familiar face on the ward, the only sane one, my only contact with the outside world.

Mary stayed for about twenty minutes and then she was on her way. I envied her. All she had to do was ring the buzzer and the nurse would press the button to let her off the ward. I couldn't do that. I wanted to get control back.

My commander came and visited me a little while later that evening. She brought a friend along with her, another officer from the unit. I was calming down as my roommate was leaving, so by the time they arrived, I was really drained and all I had left was a massive headache, dizziness, a stuffed-up nose and two five-pound eyeballs that squinted involuntarily. As soon as I saw my commander's face peek through the hospital room door, I unrolled myself out of the ball I was scrunched up in on top on my covers and I felt like talking. I had told Lt. Sharples, during one of my rambling moments, many of my childhood experiences. I was honest enough, or desperate enough, at one point when we were waiting to see the psychiatrist for the first time, to share with her that plants were the only things which breathed that I wasn't afraid of. I thought of that when the receptionist came by our chairs to water the plants on the window sill behind us.

I began to cry again when I started to talk to Lt. Sharples and her friend. I couldn't help it. They seemed so sane and I seemed so crazy. I couldn't understand what was wrong with me. I asked Lt. Sharples when I'd be getting out.

"Soon, Ranaghan. You'll be getting out soon. It will be okay."

The little drugged-up Korean woman, Hishu, was pacing up and down the hall most of the time while my two visitors were there. No one ever knew what she was trying to say so no one paid any attention to her. She stopped by my door a few times along her way. She'd play with the door knob, then look up at us, and then shuffle on down the hallway in her slippers. One time she stopped by when I was in the middle of one of my hysterical fits while Lt. Sharples and her friend were still there. I was sitting on my bed like an Indian with my legs crossed, my elbows low and digging into my thighs, my upper body hunched over, and my hands reached out playing with the end of the sheet. When Hishu stopped by, babbling off at the mouth, making no sense, I looked at my commander and screamed, "These people are fuckin' crazy up here!"

There was a long silence. Then I said, very solemnly, "I must be crazy too or I wouldn't be here. . . ."

Lt. Sharples's visit was a comfort to me, but when her time to leave came, I felt abandoned, alone, chained up. Why did everyone always walk out on me? Why was I always left to fend for myself? Why was I cracking up? I sobbed for a long while and then I dozed off, my face resting in the wet pillow.

Eleven
The Painful but Safe Days

For the first time in my life I behaved in a manner the world considered normal. I was obedient and conscientious about my hygiene and my physical appearance. I had never cared so much before about looking "okay." I had always needed to be what everyone around me wasn't. On the outside, in "civilization" as they call it, I'd acted like the crazy one because normal to me seemed boring. When I arrived on Hotel 600, the nickname soldiers gave to the psychiatric ward, I had acted normal because I didn't want to be like the "crazies." This facade lasted only until the initial shock of where I was wore off. My need to be perceived as normal remained strong for a few days and then started to taper off; I was too exhausted to continue "acting as if."

But for a while I was the most perfect patient you could imagine. I tried to do everything right for fear of being found out for any minor infraction of the rules. That's how I got there, after all. I couldn't adapt to military life. I couldn't do my job properly. I couldn't take orders from authority. I was disrespectful. I was withdrawn and depressed. Now all I had to do was prove that I could follow rules very well. "I'll be perfect," I decided. "They'll know how well I am and what a mistake it would be to keep me in this nut house, and they'll let me out."

I woke up in the mornings and made sure I did everything right—made the bed up just perfect like the army expected me to, and dusted off the top of my night table. I

94

put all my personal things, which my roommate had brought me, in the top drawer. My toothbrush, toothpaste, hair brush, wash cloth, soap dish and Oil of Olay were in dress-right dress formation inside my dusted drawer. My sneakers and slippers were lined under my bed and my journal was placed under my pillow. These were the kinds of things I hadn't been able to get right in the army. I couldn't pick it up, it seemed. I had such difficulty with the simplest procedures. My life had become so overwhelming that I literally had a hard time concentrating on tasks as simple as putting some cards in alphabetical order. I'd screw up after doing it over and over again. I always had a way of attracting attention to myself and didn't mind it either. But once in the army I didn't want the attention anymore. Now, on the ward, I was desperately trying to hide, not to be noticed, not to be found out.

I was afraid to take a shower for the first few days. I thought Hishu would attack me in the shower so I stayed unwashed until I was sure she was harmless. I ate some parts of the hospital breakfast, mostly just the sweet foods, like French toast with plenty of syrup and cereal with plenty of sugar. Somehow the smell of eggs in the hospital made me nauseated. I took my breakfast tray to the far corner of the eating area so I could eat in peace, away from the psychotic patients, far enough away so that they could not talk to me or touch me. But Hishu was always a threat, regardless of where I sat. She wandered about constantly and she was not afraid to bother anyone. The staff had some difficult nights trying to put her to bed. Sometimes they'd be too tired to deal with her so they'd give her a tranquilizer for the night.

One morning Hishu came up and started looking at the food on my tray as if deciding what she was going to choose from it. She saw I was eating the French toast and she mumbled something in her language and moved on to the next person's tray. She had her own plate. It was sitting by itself, and it had the same food on it that my tray had. Maybe she was just checking to see if everyone got the same thing? Though I was growing quite fond of Hishu and enjoyed having her around, it was difficult to ignore, at meal times, one of her physical attributes; rotting, brown teeth and the foul odor that permeated the air around her when she opened her mouth. I lost my appetite when she came over to my table.

Group therapy was the most interesting part of the day. It lasted for an hour, from 9 A.M. to 10 A.M. That was when people got picked to speak if no one volunteered. Two counselors ran the meeting, a husband and wife team from the psychology department. It was amazing to see how many people opened up when they got into the group and heard someone else speak about the same problem they had. *Group is where I can tell who is really out of touch with reality,* I thought to myself.

Comparing myself to the more unfortunate ones became my way of consoling myself on the mental ward. Thus a feeling of gratitude for not being "that bad" became my escape from the truth about myself. How convenient it was to forget that there was a reason for my being there, in the same place as the others. We were all ill, to some degree. Some were schizophrenic, others borderline psychotic, and others alcoholics and drug addicts. Group therapy was the only place one could learn about the other patients on the ward because no one opened up about themselves outside the doors of group, at least not verbally anyway. Most of us were isolates who kept to ourselves, though there were a few men I became pretty good friends with after I was up there a couple of days. We played some card games, puzzles, Monopoly and Ping-

Pong. But despite friendly relations, I kept an aloofness about me. How could I look around at the people on the ward and call them my equals? That would have meant that I was crazy too. "Crazy" and "having problems" meant the same thing to me, so I could never admit I had a problem because in my own mind that would have immediately qualified me as insane.

I went to group therapy faithfully for ten days. It was mandatory, but I noticed that patients would often be missing. During these sessions I took on the counselor role. I probed others for answers, hoping that they'd see the light and discover something about themselves that would help them get better. At the same time, I was sharing bits and pieces of my past and that was helping me discover things about myself. I was too scared not to try. I was too scared to sit quietly without saying anything. I was seesawing between a life of sanity and a life of insanity. In group therapy I began to reveal my family history, sharing part of that history with the group. But I wasn't yet engaging the material on the emotional level I would later come to grapple with because this sharing was only the beginning, just recollections. It did, however, manage to dredge up more emotions than I had anticipated it would. I was utterly confused about why these memories suddenly seemed to be so alive and vivid when they never had been before. They seemed to have come out of nowhere and they seemed to be unrelated to my life as a miserable 22-year-old soldier. I felt free enough to reveal some of my thoughts and experiences to the group.

"You know I used to lock myself in the bathroom and sometimes sleep on the bathroom floor because I was afraid if I opened it, the crazy man who chased me in there would be waiting to beat me over the head with his fists. That's the man my mother married after only knowing him for two weeks. My real father died when I was seven and after he died I found myself acting out my rage. I spent a lot of time behind locked doors screaming like hell until I was blue in the face, until my mother slipped a quarter under the door for me to buy myself the ice-cream cone I was screaming for. At other times I'd bang my head against the wall until it became lumpy, banging until I was too exhausted to continue—and all the anger I felt had been taken out on myself.

"My mother didn't cope very well with my father's death. She never wanted to have so many kids and I guess she was overwhelmed by the responsibility. She was always depressed, even when my father was alive, but once he was gone, she started to go out to the bars and sometimes she wouldn't come home. She was very angry, and would either hit us or walk out on us. But one night she came home from the bar and she brought this man with her, and two weeks after she met him, they were married. He was, legally, our stepfather. He turned out to be a real brute, beating up me and my mother and my brothers and sisters whenever he felt inspired to do so.

"One night when I was pretending to be asleep he came in with my mother at about four in the morning. I was mad because he took my little sister out to the bars with him and I wanted her to stay home with me where she'd be safe, so I turned over all the furniture in the house and I knocked the pictures off the walls and I left a nasty note on my mother's bed. The note said: 'Mother fucker busted titty two balled bitch.' Harry—my stepfather—came in and before he even saw the note, he saw the furniture and he came in and whipped me out of the bed. He started beating the pulp out of me, threw me to the ground and then pulled me by the hair to the corner of the room. In the corner he punched me in the stomach

98

over and over again. He held my hair with one hand and punched me with the other. I kept scrunching up to protect myself, but he pulled my hair so hard in the other direction that he always got his fist into my gut.

Then he started kicking me. He kicked and punched and pulled and yelled all the while that I was a spoiled brat and would never do something like this again. I kept yelling, 'I didn't do it! I didn't do it!' And he kept yelling, 'Yes, you did. I know you did! You did it! You're the only one in this house who would do something like that!' He beat me until he was too tired to continue. He was out of breath. The beating itself wasn't as bad as knowing that my mother was standing in the doorway waiting for him, holding his cigarette for him until he was finished with me. She was helpless. He'd kill her if she intervened. He finally left me, doubled up in the corner of the room gasping for breath. When he left my room my mother handed him his cigarette and he said to her, 'That takes care of her!' Then they went into the bedroom and found the note I had left her.

" 'Look at this,' Harry screamed. 'I'm not finished with her yet, that little bastard!' I heard my mother say, 'Just leave her alone. She had enough for tonight. Get her in the morning.' I felt that was her best attempt to protect me.

"I didn't hear much more except him saying, 'Yeah, I'll get her in the morning. I'll get her for this one, alright!'

"I wasn't sure if he'd remember in the morning. He wasn't very consistent and he never kept his word, but I didn't want to take the chance so when the morning came, I didn't wait around. I was the first one up and out of bed and out the door. I ran in fear, darted toward the door and out into the hallway. I didn't wait for the elevator. I ran

99

down the fourteen flights of stairs. I was so afraid he would hear me and get up and come after me.

"I got to school and my hair was in knots and my uniform was all wrinkled from sleeping in it. I usually slept in my uniform because I was always the last one up in the mornings. I slept a lot as a kid. It was an escape for me. I slept when I got home from school right up until dinner time and then I'd go back to sleep after dinner. This was before Harry arrived on the scene, like when I was in third and fourth grade, about eight years old. When Harry came around I was in the fifth grade and I started to spend a lot of time out of the house after school. Sometimes I was in the park outside of school, climbing trees and jumping at the chance every time someone dared me to do anything. I became a tough street kid, out there intimidating all the weaklings. I was so abusive to the other kids and they were afraid of me. I had one friend in school. She and I would spend our lunch hour walking back and forth behind the park house with our heads down and our eyes scanning the dirt ground for dimes, nickels, quarters, any spare change which might have been dropped by some other kid running by during his or her game of ring-o-levy. Then my one friend moved away in the middle of the school year and I had no friends. That's when I began to spend my lunch hour disrupting hopscotch games in the park. I was never playing the game, only disrupting it, and no one ever knew what to do about it so I just kept disrupting. I never fit in in grammar school. I always felt like the outcast. I tried to intimidate other kids because I had a need to at least be noticed, if not accepted."

The group leader interrupted me. "It sounds like you survived a whole lot of trauma. You must have felt very

unprotected as a child. That probably is a very frightening feeling, isn't it?"

"Yeah; well, the police were constantly at our door because the neighbors were always complaining that there was so much noise and screaming coming from our apartment. The first night that Harry and my mother were married, he punched her face. She was bleeding all over the apartment. One time he went to punch her and she ducked and his fist went through the wall. It was horrible. It's horrible to remember. They left us kids in the apartment that night and went out to the bar. My mother had a black eye and a big fat lip and then she didn't come back home that night. Harry came home without her and he was yelling all morning that our mother was a tramp and that she took off with someone else. We were really scared. We didn't know if she was ever going to come home again. And Harry was dropping pills into her drinks. My mother was always really out of it. All of us kids blamed Harry for the state my mother was in.

"Then Harry started to beat us kids too. Once he beat my older brother up because he thought he had taken the needle out of the record player. He punched him in the stomach, flung him against the wall. We couldn't do anything about it. We were all screaming to leave him alone and all I remember was Nat saying, 'Please, don't! I didn't do it. I swear I didn't do it.' But that fuckhead went and punched him right in the stomach and then kicked him in his balls. Nat keeled over. He couldn't talk or breathe. Harry left him there in the corner of the living room. We were all screaming and crying and he said, "Shut up, all of you, or you'll be next!" I felt so bad for Nat, like it was really me being beaten on and not him."

This memory was traumatic, but I continued telling it rather matter-of-factly.

101

"I felt so bad for my brother because he was such a lost and confused soul anyway. He was shattered when my father died. He was the oldest son and firstborn, and he was the closest to my father of all us kids. Once my father died, Nat got progressively worse. He went on to drop out of high school, and then started drinking and gambling. Everyone hated him because they felt like he was wasting his life away and he didn't have to. He became a really isolated, lonely soul, angry, untrusting, and unwanted. I feel bad telling this because I hated him too at that time because he used to steal money from me. But now I feel bad for him."

"How long did this abuse go on for you, Denise?" the woman counselor asked.

"A couple of months. Every time the police came to our door they would say there was nothing they could do about it and then they'd leave because my mother never wanted to press charges. One night when the police came I was screaming at the officer: 'He threw the puppy down the incinerator! He's gone! He's dead!' The officer just stood there staring at me dumbfounded, like I was crazy. Harry found a puppy or someone in the bar gave it to him. He brought it home that night, then got pissed and threw it down the incinerator at the end of the hall. It was a beautiful white puppy, the cutest thing you'd ever seen, and I always wanted a dog. For a few short minutes, I imagined I had one because it was sitting there in front of me, in my apartment. That was the worst.

"I remember another time when Harry beat my mother up and then forced her to have sex with him—I only know because I was awake all night and they were drunk and left the door to their bedroom open and my room was right next to theirs. I saw him lying on top of her naked and the bed was shaking around and then I saw my mother get up when he rolled over and fell asleep. She had no clothes on and she went to the kitchen and took a few good slugs of whiskey. When she came back to the bedroom she saw me in the hallway and she said, 'He's a disgusting pig!' She went into her room and put some clothes on and then she came to my room and said, 'What should we do? We have to get out of here or he'll kill us all. What should we do?'

" 'We should go down to Papa's. Papa can help us,' I told her.

" 'But what if he wakes up?'

" 'Forget it,' I said with great urgency. 'Let's go now while he's still sleeping. Now or never. Let's go!'

"My mother and I raced out the door. She was terrified, so was I. We kept turning around to make sure he wasn't coming down the block after us. He was capable of anything. As my mother and I ran, I had flashes in my head of the time I came out to the kitchen in the middle of the night to get a glass of water and he was straddled on top of my mother on the living-room floor, strangling her. Her face was purple. I screamed in terror when I saw this and for some strange reason Harry got up off her. Screaming never stopped him before. It usually inspired him, but this time he got up and then pointed over to me and said, 'You just saved your mother's life, you know that?' And so if he had found out that my mother had left the apartment without his permission, he would have killed her, even in the middle of the street. She wasn't allowed to go anywhere without him and she couldn't speak to anyone on the phone because he thought she would ask someone for help.

"My grandfather took us to the police station where the police officer pulled out Harry's record. He had been arrested for assault, theft, and many other felonies. The police took me and my mother to the apartment, and we all packed our bags and my grandfather drove us upstate to my mother's brother's house. Harry was left with the apartment because the police couldn't kick him out. He had managed to have the apartment lease and my mother's welfare benefits signed over to him, so until it was straightened out, the apartment was legally his.

"We stayed with my uncle for about a week, and when we came back, the apartment was totally destroyed. All the new furniture he bought on a whim with our social security checks was destroyed. The couch was torn to shreds, the tables were broken, the chair seats were slit, the cabinet doors were all ripped off, the mirrors in the bathroom were shattered, our jewelry boxes were smashed and the jewelry was thrown all over the room.

"We thought for sure then that Harry was gone for good and my mother was finished with him, but one night he reappeared, and my mother was drinking, and she let him back in. He was worse than ever. He chased me around the kitchen table with a butcher knife. He tore the telephone off the wall so I couldn't call the police, and he took all the locks off the bathroom doors so we couldn't escape into them. And we had to live with him again for months because my mother let him in. She didn't know what she was doing.

"Finally, our aunts and uncles decided to intervene. They had come to my brother's grammar school graduation party. It was a blistering hot day in June and my mother was wearing a heavy wool sweater and sunglasses. After she had a few drinks she didn't care enough to hide so she changed into a sleeveless blouse and took her sunglasses off. Our relatives saw then that her arms were all bruised and her eyes were blackened. She got beat really badly that night after all the company had left. Harry was furious that she had let everyone see her bruises so he went to work on her. He knocked her onto the floor in the bathroom, sat on top of her and smashed her head against the side of the bathtub. He told her that if she screamed or cried he'd kill her.

"But," I continued, "our relatives began calling regularly after the graduation when they saw my mother all beat up and bruised. When they called, all of us kids would tell them what was happening. They realized the severity of the problem and met with my grandparents. Shortly afterward they took all of us kids away. We were all sent to live with different aunts and uncles. Only my mother was left with the monster. I moved in with my aunt and uncle and I wound up living with them for a couple of years."

There was a long silence when I stopped talking. Everybody in the group was staring at me. I fantasized that it was because I looked like a nice Irish girl from a nice Irish family and they never imagined that I had witnessed and experienced such abuse. Or maybe they were waiting to hear how my life became a bed of roses once I was rescued by my relatives? Or maybe they were remembering their own traumatic childhoods. I don't know, because no one said anything. I couldn't really tell if anyone cared or if they were just tired of hearing me talk.

As they sat, silently, I remained quiet also, reexperiencing the pain of one particular incident. I sat there in the group seeing my mother's face as clearly as if she were right in front of me. I'd never forgot my mother's face the time she was standing by the kitchen cabinet and Harry came out of nowhere and smashed her so hard on the side of the face that her head jerked and the other side of her face smashed against the cabinet. It was such an unexpected blow. All of a sudden, he stood up, lunged toward her and punched her and then yelled, "There. There's no food in the house. That's for not bringing any food into the house." I remember the expression on my mother's face because I was sitting right in front of her and she looked right at me. She was drunk. Her eyes had big black bags under them. Very slowly, she lifted her hand and put it over her cheek where she had been punched. Her mouth slowly turned down and with a helpless, pathetic look in her eyes, she started to cry like a baby. And she was looking at me. I felt so bad for her. Again, I felt like I was the one who had been hit in the face. I wanted to help her. She was looking at me, asking for help. At times it was more painful to watch someone else getting beat up than it was to endure getting beat up myself. Not being directly involved in the action, but having to look on in horror, most helplessly, was the worse.

Each morning on the psych ward we followed the same routine, arriving in our robes and slippers to sit in the waiting area by 6:30 A.M. Before breakfast we had a group discussion led by our president, secretary, and treasurer, all of whom were fellow patients. The president kept us all updated on the daily events and enforced the rules. The secretary took notes at all the morning meetings, and the treasurer took care of funds for the sodas and candy bars at night. The nursing staff attended this morning meeting. After two days on the ward I was nominated and voted in as secretary. I didn't want to have anything to do with it. I thought *Wow! Secretary of the psychiatric ward! You're really moving up in life!* I was still telling myself that the rest of the patients on the ward were really nuts, but me, I got there by accident, by a gross mistake. "They belong here! I don't!" I didn't want to be like them in any way and I cursed their stupid system. I was ashamed and humiliated to have been elected secretary of the "psychos." That's all they were to me, psychos, even though I was in the same boat as them. At first I refused to be the secretary, but after some coaxing from the others, I became tired of listening to them and finally just shouted: "Alright! I'll do it! I'll do it, damn it! Give me the fuckin' book!"

After the group meeting we had breakfast. I always ate the same thing. We received a menu the night before and we picked what we wanted to eat from it. It was always eggs or French toast and I always ordered the French toast.

I read my big book from Alcoholics Anonymous in between group and lunch. It was my bible while I was up there and I carried it with me everywhere I went, even to the bathroom.

In the afternoon we had occupational therapy. I worked at making a plaque of birds in a circle. You had to hammer the nails into a wooden board and if you followed the instructions the nails made a picture of birds. I grouped the nails together and it made a picture. I loved to make things. It made me feel creative. I always kept busy for the whole hour of occupational therapy. I worked straight through, always hoping to finish my picture by the end of the session, but it took me the whole time I was in the hospital to work on my birds and even then, it was still not completely finished. It was more work than I thought it would be.

We also had a class in the afternoon. Someone usually came to the hospital to give us a class. Each day the topic was different. One day it was a class on stress, another on drugs and alcohol, another on feelings. I didn't mind the classes. I always liked learning something even if it was something I had already been exposed to.

From 3 P.M. to 5 P.M. we were free again. We weren't supposed to be in our rooms, but I always retreated to my room and slept for the two hours before dinner. I either slept or wrote, but I always spent the time alone. Every opportunity I had to be alone, I used to nurture my loneliness. I didn't want to be where I was and I needed a friend. When I had time to think about it, all I felt was the shame of having wound up in a place like this. I was sure I didn't belong, and yet, I was sure there was something terribly wrong with me and I needed to find out what it was.

After dinner, I usually watched a movie for a little while in the TV room. A different movie was showing every night, but I never sat through a whole picture. TV bored me. I'd rather write or draw, so I'd retreat again to my room and either draw a picture or write in my journal. On most nights while I was on the psychiatric ward a friend from AA came and picked me up to take me to a meeting. I was allowed to go after I had been there for a few days and they felt sure I was not a danger to myself. As long as I had an escort I was allowed to sign out. I looked forward to this each evening. I felt so free going down in the elevator and waking through the parking lot to a car. It was amazing to realize how much I took for granted until I was stripped of all my rights. I didn't even have the right to throw my own clothes over my back.

When I returned from AA meetings, I was always in a better mood, even if only temporarily, and I associated with the others on the ward. I'd get involved in a card game or a game of Ping-Pong. I didn't even mind being where I was because people in AA told me they'd been there too and everybody goes through different things trying to stay sober. They all seemed happy and fairly stable so I felt hope that if they had gone through what I had gone through, or something similar, and had made it, then maybe I could make it too.

Once in a while Vedo would come along to a meeting with me. He was a fellow patient on the floor who was an alcoholic and a drug addict and he had slipped while in treatment at the rehabilitation center. He was about to be chaptered out of the military. There was a chance he would be sent back to treatment and start over, but it never happened. Vedo was on tranquilizers so he couldn't always go to meetings because sometimes he was too out of it. But he didn't always want to go anyway. He had an "I don't care what happens to me" attitude. At the same time, he was not depressed. In fact, he was very upbeat and happy most of the time. Vedo and I talked often. He said I didn't seem like an alcoholic and it was hard for him to imagine me drunk. I said to him that half the people in AA didn't look like alcoholics and I couldn't image *them* drunk.

I came to feel I was protected and safe on the "nut-cracker suite." I had no responsibilities and no one expected anything from me. It was low key and undemanding and I grew to like it there after all. I made a few friends. One was Susan, a woman with schizophrenia. She had a room at the very end of the hall. No one really talked to her. Everyone was afraid of Susan because she was bizarre at times. But I remembered that during a group session, she had mentioned something about how as a teenager, she had gotten drunk and blacked out, so I thought we had something in common to talk about. I started to go down to her room to chat each night. She didn't always make a lot of sense and she had trouble following a train of thought. Sometimes I'd leave her my big book when I went out to a meeting at night.

She seemed interested. I told her she could get better too, but she had to believe it. Susan had more problems than alcoholism, but I figured she could benefit from the program too. I remember she used to mutilate herself and then not remember doing it. While she was on the ward, she slashed her wrists with a razor and when questioned about it in group, she denied having any memory of doing it. No one knew where she got the razor because we were all stripped of those kinds of items when we were admitted to the ward. So when the nurses found her sitting on top of her bed in a pool of blood from her slashed wrists, and no razor or sharp instrument in sight, it became the mystery of the floor.

Hishu became another friend of mine. She sat still for me for a whole hour one night while I drew her portrait for her. She really liked it and I felt so good giving it to her and seeing she could recognize herself in the drawing. She thought I drew her face fatter than it really was, though. She told me by pointing to my picture and then puffing her cheeks out with air from inside her mouth. Sometimes she would smile too. When Lt. Sharples came to visit me one night, she and Hishu sat down together and filled out her menu for breakfast. Hishu never filled her menu out, but Lt. Sharples was able to communicate with her and get her to say what she wanted for breakfast. Hishu usually handed in a blank sheet of paper.

I didn't have any pressures on the psych ward in terms of responsibility toward others. But my internal world was being turned upside down. My secrets were seeping out in group therapy. Some came out through my incessant, uncontrollable rambling and some were being thrown up from the depths of my being. It seemed I could no longer live in my own miserable abnormal world, thinking it was right and normal. I was left with a dreadful fear that the doctors were going to find out there was something else wrong with me besides my alcoholic identity. In reality, they already had. I started to think about that idea; I had heard about alcoholism being a symptom of other problems.

Twelve
Returning to the Unit

The ten days went by too fast and it was time for me to return to work. I was just beginning to like it up there on the psychiatric ward. I watched many patients come in and out the doors. Most stayed only for a day or two and then they were shipped off to the States or sent back to their units. Hishu left about four days before me. She was being sent back to Washington (D.C.) for further evaluation. I never got a chance to say good-bye to her because she left early in the morning when I was in the shower. I didn't even know she was leaving. I was the only one who was left up there for such a long period of time. Ten days is a long time in the military. I was beginning to get a little worried, but not worried enough to ask to be released and sent back into the jungle. To me, the army was a jungle. My military experiences, although limited, had been very unpleasant.

I saw the psychiatrist only twice over the ten-day period I spent in the hospital. One of those times I never even got out of bed to see him. He arrived unannounced, sat at my bedside and asked me how I was feeling while I lay in bed staring at the ceiling, only seeing him from the corner of my eye. He was very busy and his reply to my question about his not having time to speak with me was: "We're army doctors. You have no idea how many patients we get every day. We don't have time for individual therapy. We just evaluate you. The nursing staff observes your behavior for a few days. We get reports from the nurses and from your group therapist and then we make a decision about what would be the best thing for you. Most of the patients we get in here either get put out of the military or they get medevacked back to the States."

And there was no more special attention from Lt. Sharples either. She visited me every night on the ward, except one night and that was because they were having an alert the next morning. When she came the evening after the alert, she looked strange. She looked all messy, like she had slept in her uniform or something. I didn't like to see Lt. Sharples like that because she didn't seem like herself. I asked her what had happened to her hair and she said, "Oh, I had to pin it up because of the alert, Ranaghan." Her hair was falling out of the braid all around her head. I wanted her to fix her hair so she would look like the Lt. Sharples I knew. Her distraught appearance made me uneasy. I wanted her to stay the same and look all pulled together all the time.

When Lt. Sharples came to visit me she usually came with her friend, but a few times she came alone. I had liked it when she came alone because then we'd talk and laugh together. When her friend came along, she always interrupted our conversations. She was just joining in on them really, but I perceived it as interrupting.

The afternoon came when I was told that I would be returning to my unit to go back to work and that I would be going into the Residential Treatment Facility for alcoholics in a few weeks. They told me I'd be leaving the ward the next day. They called Lt. Sharples in and she came with her friend, Lt. Compton, and Dr. Cambridge took the three of us into a conference room and told us what was going on for me: "You are just one of those eccentric people we get up here on the ward every once in a while. You will go back to your unit tomorrow and you are on the waiting list to get into the Residential Treatment Facility. Sometime in March you will go through the six-week treatment program. My recommendation to you is to continue to attend your AA meetings and do what you're told to do in your unit. This is the army, you know. You pay for your mistakes in the army. You can't just do whatever you feel like, you know."

That's funny, I thought to myself. *I just had an emotional breakdown and the shrink tells me I'm just one of those eccentric people.* Is cracking up a mark of eccentricity? I never knew psychiatry was so focused on the actual mistakes people made, rather than on helping these people understand why they made the mistake and how to prevent it in the future for the purpose of improving their quality of life. It seemed to me that this military psychiatrist was more of a soldier than he was a psychiatrist.

I was not so sure as the psychiatrist was, that what I had done was a mistake. It seemed more like an emotional breakdown than a calculated error. The only mistake I could think of was the mistake of joining the military in the first place. And, I thought, while the psychiatrist was busy informing me that I had to pay for my mistakes, he had no problem labeling me under one of his psychiatric terms. I was not a patient with a personality disorder. I was a soldier, a piece of government property that was malfunctioning; and the reason I was malfunctioning was that I did not easily slip into the military lifestyle.

While I pondered this idea I also thought over the fact that I was the only one in the unit paying for these so-called "mistakes." Everyone else was apparently doing just fine. They all seemed to have made the adjustment that I was having tremendous difficulty making. And that, I knew, was a complex issue which could not be explained after a half-hour interview and a ten-day stay on the psychiatric ward. Yet I still was aware that I wanted what other soldiers appeared to possess: discipline, dedication, and attention to detail. At the same time I questioned whether the discipline other soldiers experienced was simply a false sense of security rather than true discipline, since a good number of the soldiers in my unit didn't know why they believed in the military system. They only knew that they were a part of it, for a variety of reasons; and because they were a part of it, they were obligated to conform and respect its every wish, if for no other reason than because the first sergeant said so.

Lt. Sharples brought me flowers that afternoon. Lt. Compton had brought me popcorn and sodas the night before. I thought my flowers were roses when I first opened them. I didn't know too much about flowers and I exclaimed in my excitement over receiving them, "Oh, roses!" Then I looked more closely and saw they were carnations. All the same I was grateful to Lt. Sharples. She helped me find a vase and put some water in it for the flowers.

The next morning I was reminded by the nurse that I'd be leaving that afternoon to go back to my unit. I procrastinated as long as I could. I did all the regular things that I would have done on the ward as if it were just another day. I pretended that I wasn't leaving or that just maybe something would happen at the last minute and I would be told to stay another day. Or maybe I'd just stay and they wouldn't notice I was still there. I went to physical training and I went to group. It was a Friday, and on Fridays we went bowling after group so I went along with the group that morning. I was buying time, petrified to return to my unit, not only because I didn't think I could handle it, but also because I was afraid of what people there were thinking about me. I thought they must all know I was on the psychiatric ward.

I was told three times that morning to pack my belongings because I was going back to my unit. I finally gave in after lunch and packed my bags. I still hadn't accepted or acknowledged that I was leaving. I just went through the motions. It's similar to losing someone close to you. You go through all the motions, attending the wake and the funeral and making the burial plans, but the fact that the person is *dead* doesn't actually sink in until all the chaos is over and you're left sitting in the room where you used to sit every night with the deceased person. I packed, dressed, and got myself ready to go, but I still hadn't accepted that I was going back to the same rotten situation I had left just a week and a half earlier. I didn't feel the pain until I was back in the office or in the barracks.

The group was on its way to Occupational Therapy and I decided not to tag along since the nurse reminded me again that it was time for me to leave. I called my unit from the nurse's station. For a few minutes I felt strong and determined, like a heroine who had been battered and now was coming back to life.

I called my unit and Sgt. Marx answered the phone: "HHD, 56th MP Battalion, Sgt. Marx speaking. May I help you Sir, Ma'am?"

"Sgt. Marx, it's Denise."

"Denise?"

"Yes, Denise! Ranaghan! PFC Ranaghan! Remember me? I'm coming home!"

"Oh yes, Ranaghan. We'll be over to pick you up."

"No. I'm coming home on my own. I'm leaving now!"

I had accumulated a bunch of belongings over my ten-day stay on the ward: an artist's briefcase, my uniform, my boots, and a few other things thrown into a big plastic garbage bag. It was heavy and awkward. I carried the briefcase in my right hand and threw the heavy garbage bag over my left shoulder. I then marched like a woman who had a definite destination, off the ward, alone and determined again, to do it on my own!

I said good-bye to no one. I hated good-byes and everyone was at Occupational Therapy anyway. I had no desire to say good-bye to the nursing staff. Dr. Cambridge was in the nurse's station when I left. He had his back to the door when I passed by on my way to the exit. I think he knew I was leaving and he was waiting to see if I was going to say good-bye to him. I didn't. I didn't know what to say and it didn't seem necessary to say anything. *He never did listen very well,* I thought to myself. He was a great talker, but he never listened very well. It took me some time to figure that out because I was naive and believed that because he was a doctor, a professional, he knew what he was talking about. But some of his words to me kept echoing in my head: "95 percent of prisoners have borderline personality disorder. That's where you'll wind up if you don't start cooperating with your supervisors!"

As I walked the four blocks from the hospital to the barracks on Gabes Kaserne, the bag was weighing heavily on my back. I stopped a few times along the way. My arms were getting sore. I was very determined to make it to my destination and to confidently put on my battle dress uniform for work. More than anything I wanted to be normal, to just go to work and not be locked up like a "loonie." I wanted to be like the people/soldiers I watched from the barred window of the psychiatric ward, who just looked like normal people going to work. I thought to myself, *This time I will do my best. I will look normal, I will act normal and then I will BE normal.*

I showed my identification card going through the entrance to Gabes Kaserne and then walked a few feet in. I stopped, plopped my bags on the ground in front of the building next to mine and I looked up at the building. Suddenly I thought, *WHAT? For two and a half years! Oh shit . . . Well, calm down, Denise. Just get in there and get through today. Thank God you got out on a Friday, it's only a half a day's work you'll have Saturday and Sunday off.*

I went straight to my barracks room and changed from my gray Army sweat suit into my battle dress uniform. I kept telling myself, "You only have to make it through three weeks of work. Then you will get all the help you need. Then you will find all the answers to your problems." All I wanted was for someone to give me the cut-and-dried solution to this bizarre puzzle of why I was going through such intense, confusing pain. I was scheduled to enter the treatment facility in three weeks. All I had to do was survive until then. It seemed as if my entire life was a waiting game where I was always surviving only with the hope that something, some day, some way, would take me out of this pain. I never lived in the moment. I couldn't. Each moment was too lonely, unbearably lonely and seemingly insignificant.

I went down to the basement, to the orderly room, and looked for someone to give me some work to do or to at least acknowledge that I was back from the hospital. But no one was around. I walked down the hallway and the place was quiet and deserted. Then I saw an open door at the end of the hall, the supply room. I went in there and Sgt. Babbith, the sergeant who had yelled about me being in her room when I first go to the unit, was sitting at her desk.

I asked, "Where is everyone, Sgt. Babbith?"

"Oh, everyone is off today. It's because of the Pig Bowl, the basketball Pig Bowl."

"Oh well, I guess I don't have to work after all."

"Are you back for good this time, Ranaghan?"

"No, Sgt. Babbith. I still have to go to the rehab center in a couple of weeks for a six-week program. I don't mind."

"Oh—really?"

"Yeah. Well, I'm going to go upstairs as long as no one is working today."

I walked down the hall one more time and saw Sgt. Marx in the orderly room.

"Sgt. Marx, what are you doing in here? I thought everyone was off today?"

"Ah, well, I have some work to do. Can you type this DF up here? Then you can go home."

"Yeah, sure."

I was grateful that someone wanted me to do something. It made me feel useful. I took the paper from his hand, slid it into the typewriter and began typing. I was so nervous. I didn't want to make any mistakes. It was as if my entire worth as a human being depended on whether I could perform this minor task without making any errors. I wanted to be perfect. I wanted everyone to know that I was all better and they could trust me now. It took me half an hour to type one small paragraph and put a signature block at the bottom of it. Sgt. Marx was sitting at his desk with the palm of his hand up under his chin. I thought he must have wanted to go home, but he wanted me to feel comfortable, too, and so he was very patient with me. Every time I asked him a question like, "How do you spell barracks?" . . . or "What is LTC Forman's middle initial?" he would come alive and act like that was a very good question to ask.

119

Eventually I finished the disposition form, proofread it five times and handed it over to Sgt. Marx. He said very enthusiastically, "Thank you, Ranaghan! You can go now. Have a nice weekend."

I went to my barracks room after Sgt. Marx released me, gladly changed into my jeans, and went to an AA meeting that night.

Thirteen
Admission into the Rehab

It was a grueling three weeks before I went into the treatment facility. On the morning of my admission into the rehab I was more than ready to go. I had been praying for the day to arrive. Daily living was just as bad as before I went into the hospital. Nothing clicked, nothing worked. I was depressed, withdrawn and nonfunctional.

I had a sleepless night before I left for rehab. It was unusual how it went, not unusual for me, but unusual for the typical alcoholic going into rehab. I was up at 6:00 A.M. that morning. I was scheduled to enter the treatment facility at 6:30 A.M. The facility was part of the hospital just across the street, but they were not connected, unlike for instance, a floor in the hospital. It was a separate entity within walking distance.

I had no plans for anyone to escort me to the hospital that morning. I had the sense that everyone had forgotten I was going at all because so many other things were happening. In fact, my rehab stint hadn't been discussed with my commander or anyone else in the unit in three weeks. I knew where I was going and I was probably the most willing to go as any patient could possibly be.

I dressed quickly. Having packed my duffle bag the night before, I was ready to roll first thing in the morning. I was terrified that someone was going to stop me from going, that this was a big trick, a joke on me, and I was really going to be stuck working at this unit I hated, in the lopsided state of mind I was in.

I was out the door five minutes after I woke up. I stood my duffle bag up on my handy luggage cart with my right hand holding my dress greens up on their hangers. I had one minor flight of stairs to get down and I did so with startling success. I opened the black battalion door, rolled my cart out to the street and headed to the front gate. Minutes later, I was at Miles Kaserne where the rehab was. No one in my unit even knew I had left.

It was a rainy morning. There was a light drizzle coming down, not too bad, but bad enough to keep me tugging at the plastic wrapper covering my dress greens. It was windy too. I struggled against the wind for the whole walk. I felt heroic as I walked my way to help at the rehab, as if I were really going places and getting there on my own. No one was pushing me, like they had when they locked me up on the psychiatric ward. This was all my own choice. This is what I wanted for myself. It seemed no small miracle to have gotten something I wanted for myself in the military.

I flashed my ID card at the gate of Miles Kaserne and consciously paced slowly, though my heart was pounding, toward the rehab center. All sorts of thoughts were going through my mind: *I wonder if my unit knows I left? I wonder if I'll have nice roommates? . . . Who is my counselor going to be? . . . I should be cool at first. Don't just trust anybody. Find out who's committed first. . . . I wonder what the days are like? What do we do? What if I don't get along with my roommates? I guess we'll all get used to each other. . . . I wonder if we still have to wear our uniforms every day?*

As far as I knew I was the first arrival at the treatment facility. *What a soldier,* I thought. I pulled my cart up the three steps and through the office doors. I placed it in the nearest corner I could find and threw my dress greens across the two-seated couch. Looking around for someone who could give me directions about what to do with myself, I walked through another door and saw a man in an army uniform typing. I approached him:

"Excuse me."

"Yes."

"Where do I go? I am supposed to be admitted here today."

"What's your name?"

"Denise Ranaghan."

The sergeant directed me to walk across the street to the central hospital, pick up my medical records, and then walk down to the flower shop in the hospital and wait in the chairs in front of the flower shop until the staff came in at 7:00 A.M. I would get my blood checked at the lab across from the flower shop and then come back over to the facility.

Quite a few people were waiting there when I arrived. I signed in and took my seat. I looked at those around me. Some of the faces I saw were faces I wound up looking at for the next six weeks. . . .

The light-skinned black girl sitting right next to me looked pretty angry. I was hoping she wasn't there for the same reason I was because the thought of having to spend six weeks with an angry-looking person like her caused me immediate anxiety. As I sat there I soon became amused by my own stream of consciousness. I had always had a problem with laughing out loud because of my own inner thoughts so people usually thought I was pretty strange. I started to laugh alone as I was sitting next to this girl. While she could have been a very nice person, I had already packaged her up and pushed her away just because she appeared angry and I felt a little intimidated by her. (Already I was arranging the play and the players in the show!) I thought I'd say hello. I had nothing to lose.

"Hi. My name's Denise."

"Maria."

That was enough for now. Maria was sitting there with her specimen cup in her hand. Although I had been given one too, when I signed in with directions to fill the cup to the line as soon as possible, I never could urinate when commanded to do so. Actually, I never could do *any*thing when commanded to do so.

I sat there for an hour and a half before I could go. By this time Maria had left. She had gotten angry at the lady who tried to get in front of her in the line. She said she'd been sitting there 45 minutes and she was getting out of there, and she did.

I had nothing to hide on the urinalysis. I hadn't had a drink in eight months. My blood was clean, alcohol-free. I wasn't dependent on alcohol—I was just having a terrible time trying to live without it. I had been living in a shoe-box until I joined the army and was forced to come out of my box. I didn't experience the military to be the ideal environment in which to climb out of a box and found myself suspicious and fearful of all that existed outside of that box anyway. When I was in my unit a sergeant came up to me and said, "Denise, I'd like to take you out to dinner tonight. How 'bout it?"

I thoughtlessly and fearfully snapped back, "Who put you up to this? What do you want from me?" I suspected the individual had ulterior motives and I could not believe that anyone would actually want to take me out, especially not someone in my chain of command. It was against the rules and since rules were the only source of structure in my otherwise chaotic world, I reminded everyone of what they were and I clung to them most rigidly myself.

I handed in my specimen bottle with a smile on my face, and returned to the rehab facility as directed. I was being very obedient, doing what I was told to do. That was unusual behavior and whenever I did what I was told I was very conscious of it and there was always a reason. This time it was because I didn't want to screw things up. I wanted to get better, to figure this mess out.

On my way back to the Residential Treatment Facility (RTF), I passed Maria walking back toward the hospital. By now I knew we were both going to the same place for the same reason. She was walking quickly back toward the hospital. I pasted on a phony smile and said, "Hello again." She put on a plastic smile and returned the hello. I was thinking that we were both probably intimidated by each other. She was probably praying that I wasn't her roommate too. Neither of our prayers was very helpful; we were assigned as roommates.

I reported back to the sergeant to find out what my next mission would be, and he escorted me to my room, which had four beds in it. (So much for my privacy.) I guessed I wasn't going to be able to isolate myself like I did every time I got the opportunity to.

"Who gets the desks?" I asked. "There are only two desks and four beds. I do a lot of writing, you know."

"You can have that desk and that bed in the corner there," the sergeant answered. Then he said, pointing to the locker at the foot of the bed, "That's your locker. Don't forget you're in the military and you are to maintain a military appearance at all times. Your room as well as your personal appearance is to be military at all times. This is no vacation! We have a formation every morning at 7:45 A.M. and you are to have finished breakfast and be in full uniform, spit-shined boots and a pressed uniform."

"Yes, Sergeant."

Well, I thought, *I didn't assume I was going on vacation!* I felt tremendously relieved to be getting away from all the military robots I had been working with. I kind of hoped I was on a six-week self-improvement plan, not another "become a better soldier" training camp. Believe me, basic training and advanced individual training were more than enough military living than I needed for a lifetime.

I was as military as I was capable of being, but although it was the best I could do at that time, unfortunately that wasn't very military. I was convinced I was not meant to be a soldier, so—naturally—I was not good at it. I believed I was a failure as a soldier, worthless, confused, stupid. But somehow, I also knew deep down inside I would someday learn who I was. I had this bubbling, unsatisfied desire to find out what I was all about, and what this game of life was all about. Something inside of me was relentlessly demanding my attention.

A little later on that first morning our group of eight met with the staff at the RTF. There were three tracks in the RTF. Track one was the newest group of soldiers in the hospital; track two was two weeks into the program and track three was four of the six weeks through. Every Friday at 1 P.M. track three had a completion ceremony. All commanders of the "graduating" soldiers gathered while the soldier spoke about her experience of the program. Each soldier introduced herself as an alcoholic and told about what it was like before she went into treatment, what had happened and how she felt at the present. Most usually thanked their counselors and their commanders.

So our messy-looking group met with the staff that morning. The staff went around the table and introduced themselves and told us a little about themselves. Then they asked us to do the same. Most just said their names and answered yes or not to the questions directed at them. When my turn came I introduced myself. I said; "My name is Denise and I'm an alcoholic." I had learned that line from the AA meetings I had attended before I went to the hospital. I felt proud again, cocky because I knew that was the right answer. I was supposed to be an alcoholic, wasn't I? Isn't that what I was there for? The next question was a little more difficult. A thin, intellectual-looking man with a beard who was sitting at the other end of the table asked me, rather quickly and rudely I thought, why I was here. I hadn't even finished the whole of my first sentence. I was in the middle of the word "alcoholic" when he popped in with, "What are you here for, Denise?"

Gee, I thought to myself, *that's a tough one. Why am I here? I think it's because I'm the alcoholic I identified myself to be, but if I haven't had a drink in eight months and all these people sitting around me have baggy, bloodshot eyes, shaky hands, and tapping feet, while I sit here as healthy as Jane Fonda, then why am I here?*

I felt suddenly very humiliated and found myself at a loss for an answer. I never did respond. I just looked up at this man who I had already decided was a total idiot, and the counselors moved on to the soldier sitting next to me.

After that soldier introduced himself the first meeting was over. I stood up slowly and walked out of the room staring at the floor. I felt confused again. Every time I started to feel there was a reason for all this, some "jerk" would say something, anything, and I'd be right back where I started from; self-doubting, confused, and angry at one more person. It didn't take much to confuse me. "Hello" was enough, sometimes. To a "hello," I was likely to respond suspiciously. "What do you mean, 'hello'?"

I was conscious of the intellectual with the beard watching me as I walked out the door. I wanted to pluck his beard off, one painful, stubborn hair at a time. But I was afraid of him, too.

That "intellectual" turned out to be my counselor for the next six weeks.

Fourteen
Hard Feelings

The first few days in the rehab were pretty routine. I felt very anxious. I was itchy to get better, asking myself when the miracle was going to happen, not yet realizing that I had been living the miracle. Since I was in too much psychic pain to continue functioning, and was forced to break down completely, the miracle began when I could no longer deny I had a problem. I had to begin to look inward for answers; my miracle was going to be a long one and not the type that lends to instant gratification or gratitude. I heard people in AA talk about the miracle in their lives and so I figured something very good was going to happen to me very soon. I didn't think it would take much work, just some counseling and a few days' rest.

Group therapy, from 8 A.M. to 9 A.M., was the most intense part of treatment. We were a group of eight alcoholics with eight sets of problems stemming from the same pitiless disease. Mr. Sherwood and Dan T. were the team counselors.

Dan was a recovering alcoholic, a physically big Hungarian man with bulging eyeballs and a voice that boomed. When Dan spoke, everyone listened. He also had a terrible habit of sucking all the phlegm out of his nostrils back down through his throat every couple of minutes or so. I assumed that loud obnoxious habit meant that he had some sinus trouble, but I was sure he could have been more discreet about it. Although it was so disturbing in the beginning, once I got to know Dan, I forgot

129

about it, even though he never stopped doing it. We'd be in the middle of a conversation and all of a sudden he'd suck it all up and make that noise. After getting to know Dan, his ugly habit became just like his arm or his leg. It was a part of him and nobody questioned him about it.

Dan T. was devoted to Alcoholics Anonymous. He lived for the program. It had saved his life and it was the only way he knew of that alcoholics could recover from such a devastating, life-threatening disease. Dan talked AA day and night. He slipped it in anywhere and everywhere he could as the answer to the alcoholic's problem. Dan was one of the AA's to whom rock bottom had been a close encounter with death. He often shared his story of his many hospitalizations. His last drinking stint ended with his waking up strapped to a hospital bed, with delirium tremens, tubes stuck up his nose, and no recollection of how or when he had arrived there. The first words he had heard when he woke up in the hospital, after days of lying in a coma, had come from the doctor standing over his bed: "You're one lucky man to be alive today."

Mr. Sherwood was very different from Dan T. Mr. Sherwood was highly intellectual. He was the brain power behind the group. He worked in a quiet, calm way. Unlike Dan T., Mr. Sherwood very rarely displayed anger or lost his temper, and sometimes when Dan became too confrontative with someone, Mr. Sherwood would slip in a calm word of encouragement to cool things down. Dan had a hot temper and sometimes his "kicks in the ass" were too hard, though he'd always defend his hardness with the line: "In AA you get what you need, not what you want; and sometimes what you need is a swift kick in the ass." Mr. Sherwood never disagreed with Dan. If Dan jumped on someone, telling them they weren't trying hard enough or working the program, Mr. Sherwood would calmly slide in with, "Dan is right. You seem to be taking your treatment very casually lately. That doesn't seem like you, Chris. What's going on with you?"

Mr. Sherwood was my personal counselor. He was a good-looking man with a nicely-shaped auburn beard which covered a good part of his face (his beard was one of those very full ones), and beautiful sky-blue eyes which you'd notice before you took in anything else about him. His eyes spoke a language of their own, always giving away the frame of mind he was in, be it pensive, joyful, or disappointed. He had a small body frame for a man, standing about 5' 7", with a slightly hunched back, which somehow seemed to add character to him. On anyone else this slight hunch might have appeared unattractive, but on him it seemed to me to be almost a necessary part of the man. Everything about him conveyed a message of gentleness, understanding, warmth, and serenity. He spoke without ever raising his voice in an angry way, his tone always soft and considerate. His eyes were always analyzing as they focused on you. His calm, confident mannerisms made me feel that he knew what he was talking about and that I probably should listen to him because I might learn something.

The first group therapy session we went around the circle and introduced ourselves to each other. Words were hard to come by. The others in the group seemed shy, too. It took a few days poking and prodding from Dan and Mr. Sherwood before our group felt at ease. But there were a few group members who seemed to speak freely enough. They were the ones who had already been in the group for four weeks. There were three of us in the group from the new track.

I felt an immediate attraction to one other member in the group. David, married with one child, was a good-looking man with light brown hair, large green eyes and a charming, distinguished laugh. I really loved his laugh and after hanging around with him for long enough I unconsciously adopted it. Coming from me the laugh sounded fake, but I found myself laughing that way even though it didn't fit me and was not genuine.

David was fun to be around. He was a natural comedian, with the ability to find humor in a lot of situations, always popping up with a good joke to lighten up even the most serious situations. And yet he also had a very sensitive side which very few people knew about. I was one of those few. The temptation for the two of us to get involved sexually was always there, for the physical attraction was as powerful as I had ever experienced it to be. We talked very openly about how we felt about each other and were healthy enough to come to the decision that since David was married, it wouldn't be wise for us to become involved.

However, David was unhappy in his marriage. He found the lack of communication between himself and his wife very frustrating. She had no understanding of the disease of alcoholism and was too afraid to come to the treatment center for the two-week spouse program. Her denial was too strong and she couldn't conceive that David's drinking problem involved her. "If he quit drinking, we'd be fine," was her philosophy.

I, who had until then been totally incapable of relating to anyone because of my lack of trust and habit of extreme isolation, was finding David to be a very understanding companion. I liked him. He was funny, tough, appreciative and protective of me.

One thing I did dislike about David was his back. When we played volleyball in the gym for physical training and he'd take his shirt off, I could see the huge tattoo which covered both shoulders and went halfway down his back. I hated that tattoo. I found it frightening, and refused to look too closely at it. It was too big and too ugly to study or to inquire about. I hated it most the day David was mad at me. That day came when I was crushed because I started to get honest and he angrily turned on me. He had trusted me with something and because I felt what he trusted me with was a threat to his recovery, I felt obligated to tell his counselor. I had no choice. David had gone home on a weekend pass and had taken a sip of beer. He had told me this in confidence and insisted that I not tell a soul, but I felt I should disclose this information because we were in treatment for a disease which stole our lives and could potentially kill us, and David was still flirting with its poisonous potion.

I didn't feel comfortable with David once he told me he was drinking and he wasn't going to share it with his counselor or our group. So I broke my promise to keep my mouth shut and I spoke to my counselor about it. I told Mr. Sherwood I knew someone in our group who had been drinking alcohol on a pass, but I did not tell him who it was. This way I could rationalize that I actually did keep my promise, even though I was hoping Mr. Sherwood would figure out who I was talking about—which of course, he did. I didn't feel like a traitor. Our program was one of total abstinence. The disease was getting the better of David and I could not sit back and watch him deceive himself. I would have hurt him more by doing that.

Before I said anything to Mr. Sherwood, I told David that I was going to mention his slip, if he didn't decide to mention it himself. David was fiercely angry. His eyes filled with hate as he stared dead straight at me:

"I trusted you! You're a traitor, you fuckin' bitch!"

"David, it's for you I'm doing it! I don't want to enable

you to stay sick. If I keep my mouth shut, I might as well watch you kill yourself."

"Fuck you, man! You're an asshole! I trusted you! Never again!"

He stormed off, red hot and flaming, determined never to speak to me again. I was not used to blowing the whistle on my peers. I usually closed my eyes, plugged my ears and kept quiet. But something was changing in me. I was acting differently, taking action instead of allowing the parade to march on by. I was starting to participate. I was starting to value and express my opinion, and of course, I began to lose the friends who had liked me better with my mouth shut.

So, David was not the friend I thought he was. Once I made the independent decision not to collude in his self-destructive plan, he turned on me like a mad pit bull. He eventually got a group of his buddies to side against me, too, which made life at the treatment facility very uncomfortable for me. I was scorned and called all kinds of names ranging from Benedict Arnold to House Rat. But despite being ostracized, I had no regret about what I had done and felt no urge to abandon my position.

The issue eventually came out in a heated argument in group therapy. My body was shaking like a leaf because of my fear of David's anger. Another group member was talking about an experience that had taken place on a weekend pass and the person mentioned something that made me think of David's hiding his slip from the group. I looked at David and said, my voice tremulous,

"Yeah, one drink won't hurt, now, will it?"

David got the message immediately. Mr. Sherwood, who was David's counselor as well as mine, picked up on it immediately also. David and I stared at each other intently. His face was filled with unrelenting anger, mine with endurance. I was determined to get at the truth. David's eyes looked like they were bullets about to pop out of his head and hit me right in the forehead; not just wounding me, but killing me, shutting me up forever.

Mr. Sherwood interrupted the tension between David and me: "I'm really concerned because it's been brought to my attention that someone in this group went out and drank this weekend and did not bring it up in the group."

David's eyes darted back and forth between me and Mr. Sherwood. Then he looked at me and shouted, "I hate you. I trusted you and you betrayed me!"

I was too shaken up to defend myself, which is what I felt I had to do. It didn't dawn on me then that David was not just angry, but incredibly hurt. He had trusted me as a friend. Looking back now, I am able to see beyond the anger and hear what David was trying to say. When I think back on it, instead of feeling the self-righteous need to stand my ground I feel moved by how much David must have really cared about me to have become so angry.

Mr. Sherwood followed David's outburst: "Denise, you are shaking. Are you aware of that?"

I didn't answer him. My entire body was trembling. I wasn't really afraid of David because I knew he couldn't harm me physically, but I was emotionally distraught because he and I had been close and now I felt he was turning against me. I had never seen this angry side of him before. Yet I remembered feeling the same way he felt and I knew the anger was a huge mask covering a deep wound. As for myself, I had shared my intimate thoughts and feelings with David and now he hated me. He was my very good friend and now, I thought, it would never be the same between us. I felt like withdrawing inside myself again, where I could hide from the hurt I was feeling and where no one could hurt me further.

Mr. Sherwood turned to David. "How much did you drink, David?"

David shifted his eyes at the sound of Mr. Sherwood's voice and as he answered he looked back at me: "All I had was a sip of beer. That's all, God damn it!"

I felt David's bullet-like eyes piercing through me while I stared at the floor, still shaking. The session was almost over. Mr. Sherwood told David he wanted to talk to him after group. When group broke up David was the first one out of the room.

David had many friends and by lunch time I was receiving either dirty looks or the silent treatment from most of them. Many of the soldiers in the rehab program didn't want to be there. They were command referred and often their military career was on the line. Very few soldiers came to the program wanting to get better, but somehow it seemed that everyone, by the end of the six weeks, was moved in some way. No one left unaffected, even if it meant, for some, leaving angrier than when they had arrived. But there were a few who were frightened enough to be serious about sobriety from the beginning. Some of those individuals congratulated me for having the courage to do what I did. Others were willing to discuss it with me and were honest in telling me they would have gone about it in a different way. One person said to me: "Maybe you could have brought it up in a group instead of going behind David's back and telling Mr. Sherwood." *I didn't go behind David's back,* I thought to myself defensively. I had told David exactly what I was going to do if he didn't turn himself in or tell the group what he had done. There was a certain level of honesty we had established in the group and David was undermining it. He had chosen not to come forward himself so I chose the alternative.

David began intimidating me on a regular basis. I was very uncomfortable at physical training playing volleyball because every time he hit the ball over the net he smashed it at me really hard. He began to take on the leadership role in his group and had everybody wrapped around his finger. On one level, he was well liked because of his light-hearted personality. But I felt the other reason he was winning everybody over, manipulating them—though they were unaware of it—was that it was his way of getting even with me. He had a certain power over me now and he was getting others to take sides against me. This went on for about a week and then there was only one week left before David would leave the RTF.

To my surprise I went to my room one afternoon after lunch, just days before David was scheduled to leave the program, and I found a bouquet of flowers there with a note from David:

Dear Denise,
    I'm sorry. I respect you and I know you did what you thought was best. I would like to talk again.

David

The gratitude I felt for having been forgiven was beyond words. It was also unnecessary and excessive. Part of me firmly believed I had done nothing wrong to begin with. *David must have realized that I cared about him too much to let the whole issue slide,* I thought. Now, I believed, we could get back to being friends and having our private late night talks together. There was no question in my mind about whether I should forgive him for the abuse he had heaped upon me. I held no resentment.

It was a fantasy to believe that David and I could pick up on our relationship where we left off before this disruption. Somehow it was never the same between us. After our conflict, David and I were too careful with each other. He was careful because he didn't want to hurt me and I was careful because I desperately wanted to regain David's trust, not realizing that I already had it. We both held back our real thoughts and feelings and seemed to agree on just about everything, but our freedom to be ourselves had been lost and there was not enough time to regain it. We were headed in that direction over five or six days, but it was never quite the same. Time was too stingy with us.

I will never forget the day when I left the rehab. David came back to hear me speak. At the point when I was most nervous, I had forgotten to put my necktie on, then ran from the formation back to my room to get it. When I turned to fly back out the door in a frenzy, David was standing in the doorway. He took the bow tie from my hand and put it on for me. I felt calmer somehow and I walked back and took my place in the formation just seconds before we marched into the roller rink where each departing patient would stand in front of a group of about 150 people and tell them what the treatment program had been like for them.

Fifteen
Addiction and Confrontation

Our track did everything together throughout the day: group therapy, occupational therapy, physical therapy, classes which introduced us to Alcoholics Anonymous, classes on families and alcoholism, sexually transmitted diseases, health and nutrition, spirituality, and a variety of other related issues. My individual sessions with Mr. Sherwood were usually in the afternoon. Typically we met at least twice a week on an individual basis.

When my treatment ended I didn't want to leave Mr. Sherwood because I was afraid he'd forget me. I was afraid that the lack of his physical presence would mean the relationship never was. I wanted him to think about me all the time the way I did about him. I was jealous when I saw another patient coming out of his office, especially if the other was a female. During a class he taught us, my roommate Peggy used to gawk at him. I was sure she had a crush on him. But Mr. Sherwood wasn't her counselor. I hated to think that she might have sat in my seat on the couch in his office. I was filled with rage and anger at even the thought of it. Thank God it wasn't a reality or I really might have cracked up.

I thought about Mr. Sherwood all day long. I looked forward to my individual therapy sessions. Everything I did, I did for him. I even imagined he was watching me when I played sports, or ran, or talked to people; imagining he was watching me motivated me to do my very best, to push myself to the limit, all the while fantasizing about how proud he was of me. And it worked for me temporarily. I was happy, overflowing with energy most of the day, kind and thoughtful toward people around me, gaining insight in some areas and growing in recovery at a rapid pace. I never stopped long enough to ask why. I automatically attributed my well being, my elated moods, to the program in which I was making such progress. I didn't immediately recognize that as long as Mr. Sherwood was around, I was satisfied and fulfilled, like a baby blissfully sucking on her mother's nipple.

I was not recognizing the connection between my alcoholism and my unmet needs. Perhaps my addiction to alcohol provided a source of nurturance I yearned for from a human being while it protected me from the intensity of feelings around my need for love and my lack of willingness to receive it in what appeared to be portions too small. Mr. Sherwood's love seemed like a tease, just as, strangely enough, my first drink seemed like a tease. I would always need another and another and another, just as I would always feel I needed more and more of Mr. Sherwood. I had spent so much time in my past trying to disguise through the use of toxic substances my obsessive need to be someone else's object of love. But it never really worked. In the end what was supposed to be disguised had become highlighted. Any comfort I received from the bottle was fleeting. Unfortunately, I became addicted to those fleeting moments of ease because they were the only moments of solace I knew. It was only when those moments faded into nothingness, when the greatness of the misery buried the comfort, that I was able to see the extent of my insatiable needs and the illusions of comfort my escapes provided. I needed something, someone, and I needed all of that something or someone, and then I would need more still. This was the root of my alcoholism, of my problems, and of my unhappiness. Something inside of me relentlessly screamed to be filled. But it was a bottomless pit, and I was a bottomless pit, but had never recognized myself as such. This bottomless pit was my deep yearning to be taken care of and to be loved. I had been searching for a mother or a father to give me unconditional love and consistent guidance. But I never had known that was what I was looking for. Nor did I know that I didn't have to spend the rest of my life searching for it, that it was possible to have my needs met without sucking the life out of others, without smothering others and wishing to be smothered by them.

As all my needs shifted onto Mr. Sherwood so did the desire that he be the one to fill them. The illusion arose again, that I had found my answer to the empty pit syndrome, and so I thought of little else except my fantasies about securing this relationship. If I were left on my own, without Mr. Sherwood, I would be left empty once again.

As joyful an illusion as my days with Mr. Sherwood seemed to be at times, they were laced with a fear of abandonment. This, after all, was a short-term program. What would I do without Mr. Sherwood? How would I live without him? Why would I want to? *He has faith in me,* I thought. *He believes in me. He encourages me. He helps me discover myself. He helped me come out of a severe depression. He laughs with me. He thinks I have a nice smile and a good sense of humor. He loves me unconditionally.* These things I knew and as my time to leave treatment drew nearer, the high-as-a-kite syndrome slipped away and a fear-ridden panic emerged, followed by depression. I panicked at the realization that feeling good was not permanent and I could slip into a hopeless depression at any given time. I wondered how I could be feeling the intense fears when I was nearing the conclusion of my treatment.

After I had missed an appointment with Mr. Sherwood, he seemed angry with me and he brought it up in group:

"Denise, you knew you had an appointment with me yesterday afternoon and you took off to the PX with Peggy. Why did you do that?"

He sounded irritated. I was glad because his being irritated was better than his not caring or not noticing that I missed my appointment. Now I had the opportunity to express how I felt. Missing session was typical of my way of communicating feelings. I would act them out because I didn't know how to sit down and tell someone how I felt. Now that I had behaved wrongly, I had the attention I wanted and it still would be hard for me to tell Mr. Sherwood how I felt, but I had learned in the group that expressing my feelings was very important, even if it was a belated expression. I was, at that point, feeling very emotional, and I couldn't keep it to myself anymore. I had been walking around terrified and angry for days, unable to communicate. Now I had the chance to tell Mr. Sherwood how I felt and I was compelled to do so. I needed for him to know; I wanted him to know.

"Yes, I knew I had an appointment with you yesterday, and I purposely did not show up for it."

I stopped for a minute and I raised my eyes from the floor and fixed them on Mr. Sherwood: "I didn't show up for my appointment with you because I know I need you and I don't want to need you."

A long silence followed my confession. My lips were quivering and I artfully held back the dam of tears welling in my eyes. Mr. Sherwood stared at me. He understood. He didn't have to say anything and neither did I.

What broke the silence in the room was a remark from Jeff, another patient in the group, whose insensitivity to the feelings conveyed was obvious. Jeff was a big black soldier, about 6' 3" , and he and I were very close. We had quickly grown to be friends, more because we had grown up in the same borough of New York than anything else. Jeff was aware, to some degree, of what had transpired between Mr. Sherwood and me, and what he expressed may have reflected his own jealous feelings or his own fears of separation. With an angry and fed-up attitude, he lashed out. "You only live right around the corner! You can come here and talk to him whenever you want to. What else do you want from the man? He says he cares about you. Come on, man."

At that moment in the group I hated Jeff more than I had hated anyone before. He carelessly broke the feelings that were being communicated through the silence and the locked stares. I resented him for being jealous enough to numb himself to what was going on. Maybe I had expressed too freely his own fear, the one he was unable to express because of the tough image he had to uphold. Or it could have been that he was jealous that I had feelings for someone other than him? I will never know the answer.

Group therapy was by far the most intense hour of the day for all of us in the program, but especially for whoever happened to land in the "hot seat" that day. I specifically recall occupying the "hot seat" one morning after we had been in group for about four weeks. Dan T. came flat out of nowhere and asked me:

"Denise, were you ever beaten?"

His question seemed so threatening. I turned to him quickly and replied, "What makes you ask that?"

"Well, Denise, we've been in this group for four weeks

now and no one knows anything about you other than what you share as an answer to someone else's problem. Why are you here?"

I felt invaded, attacked, as if Dan had split me in half and was dissecting me to figure out what was wrong with me. He was right. I never shared much in group, but I shared at great lengths with Mr. Sherwood in our private sessions. I didn't particularly care to have everyone hear my problems. It didn't seem necessary. I wasn't as frightened as I had been a few weeks earlier when I was sentenced to the psychiatric ward and had managed to impulsively recount my abusive history. The flashbacks were at my fingertips then. Now I had no feelings about my past at all. Once in a while I'd share something from my past if I thought I could relate to someone else's similar experience, but other than that, only Mr. Sherwood and David, my close friend, knew what I was all about.

Dan had hit a sore spot. I was here because I needed help, yet I had spent the four weeks in group avoiding talking about myself or my history. When I did speak in group I usually did so with humor and quickly had the group laughing. I told the tales of my rebellious years in high school, how I instigated trouble on a daily basis, how I got kicked out of classes, how I was impeached from class presidency because I called Sister Aldie an asshole and how she cracked me over the head with the notebook I was using to cheat on my trigonometry quiz.

Joking around, I learned, was my way of protecting myself, of avoiding painful feelings and remaining superior to others in the group. If I knew all about their problems and they only knew the funny stories about mine, then I was invulnerable, I thought. I was able to get away with this for four weeks because I was able to come out with some startling insights which were helpful to others and so members and leaders usually became very involved in piggybacking on my insights and observations. I was so good at deflecting attention from myself that when the members of the Track who were two weeks in front of me went around the circle to say their good-byes to each person in the group, a few of them said to me, "And, Denise, I don't even know why you're here. You seem okay to me." I had established myself as the kind of person to whom people came for answers, rather than someone who needed answers from those I perceived as "sick, weak people."

Yet this position I took on for myself was a terrible trap in that it fed my loneliness and isolation. When I felt needy, I was incapable of asking for help. In addition to this, I somehow felt that by keeping my mouth shut about myself in group, my meetings with Mr. Sherwood were more special. I reasoned that if I told him about myself, things that no one else knew, then I could keep believing that he was the only one who knew me and he could remain very special. This attitude kept me from opening up and sharing with others and it led me to believe that only Mr. Sherwood could know me well enough to help me. It shut the door on numerous other sources of help.

In answer to Dan's question about why I was there I responded, "I am here because I need help. I can't live with alcohol and I can't live without it. [This was yet another memorable line I heard spoken by others in AA and it seemed to fit.] I didn't have too much trouble putting down the drink, but I've been in trouble ever since I did. I can't cope with any of my responsibilities. Getting out of bed in the morning and showing up for formations in my unit started to become difficult. And I was very depressed all the time."

I took special care to avoid the question on abuse. I

had never actually accepted that I had been abused as a child, even after it had come up on the psych ward. I almost felt as if that abusive life I talked about then had belonged to someone else. *I didn't really live through that,* I thought. That scared little child who spent ten days on the psychiatric ward lived through that, but that was somebody else, not me.

Besides, abused kids were the ones you saw on the cover of the newspapers with black eyes and broken arms and legs, or the ones you heard had been found in the garbage pails in some alleyway. My childhood was normal, I protested. I had food on my plate and more than that, I had an education. I wound up on the psychiatric ward because my education failed to insulate me against insanity as I had expected it to, but my present difficulties didn't have anything to do with what happened to me growing up. I was crazy. No one made me that way. I just happened to be that way. So, abuse? No; that was not relevant to my present troubles and I didn't want to share it with the whole group. Maybe with Mr. Sherwood I would share it if he thought it was relevant, but not with a whole group of people.

Only Dan had something else in mind. As soon as I stopped to take a breath between the sentences I was rattling off about what I was doing there, he loudly repeated his original question, this time with his tone of voice much more demanding: "Denise, have you ever been abused?"

I stared at Dan for a second and then my famous defense mechanism kicked in and took charge. My defense was my smile. I smiled and then I giggled. That always popped up whenever I might be in danger of feeling something that was unpleasant. It also took over many times in the place of tears. My smile wasn't always real. Sometimes it served as a mask, and Mr. Sherwood picked up on that the first day I arrived at the RTF. For the entire six weeks I was there, every time I smiled and he didn't see anything funny, he reminded me I was smiling and then inquired, "You're smiling. Why are you smiling?" And sometimes I really didn't know why, but the more he asked the more I had to think about it until the time came when I could say why I was smiling. Most of the time it was either because I was being told something I already knew, because I was crying inside, or because I couldn't deal with the feelings I was experiencing at the time. It was really odd, but I smiled at the most inappropriate times. It seemed to be an involuntary reaction. And other people found it odd and confusing as well.

So I smiled in Dan's face and Dan just wasn't as polite as Mr. Sherwood. Being a recovering alcoholic himself he knew many of the twists and turns of the mysterious disease of denial and what it does to its victims. Dan, blunt as ever, asked, "What the fuck are you smiling at?"

That certainly didn't wipe the smile off my face. It made me laugh very hard. Dan stared at me until I finished laughing. I was the only one laughing. I was embarrassed once I stopped. This was my life we were talking about and I was too scared to crumble down and shatter the pieces of my past that turned me into a fiercely angry reactor when faced with any small thing at all. I still had a silly grin on my face.

Dan waited patiently. Finally he said; "Look, honey. You can laugh your ass off all you want. It's *your* ass. We're in here to help you get better. If you want to laugh you can go back out there [he pointed out the window] and laugh and you can laugh yourself right into picking up the bottle again. And believe me it doesn't get any better with the drink!"

I appreciated his anger, but it didn't move me to get honest with my feelings. Dan cared deeply about me and about every single person in the group. I knew that so I could accept his anger, and I knew he was right on the money. But somehow I never seemed to get angry at him or anyone else when I was allowed to. I always got angry at people I wasn't allowed to get angry at, like first sergeants, and in places where I wasn't allowed to get angry, like my unit.

Dan was not finished. He continued to try to evoke some feeling from me:

"Look, for some reason you are sick enough to crawl up in a little ball in the corner of your room. You shut down, take a trip way out of reality. You wind up on the psychiatric ward and then you get sent over here to us. Do you think you were on the psychiatric ward because you got it all together? No. Something is wrong. You have a chance here to do something about it, to get it out, work it out, and what do you do? You laugh! You laugh at your own fuckin' life, baby! If you don't break soon, you're gonna laugh your way right back to the psychiatric ward, maybe permanently this time. Would you like to be a vegetable locked up in a mental institution for the rest of your life?"

Dan was pressing some very sensitive buttons. He wasn't just pressing them. He was pushing them painfully hard and leaving his finger on them. I was afraid of what Dan was saying because I knew it was true. I had thought about it when I was on the psychiatric ward. My biggest fear was getting locked away for life. Yet I continued to sit there with a smirk on my face. I could not express my true feelings and I was hurting very badly inside. I could not let myself burst out with it all and get rid of it. It festered in me and I'd walk out of every group session wishing I'd had the guts to get serious and honest. I was petrified on the inside yet smiling like a Cheshire cat on the outside. It frustrated Dan. In AA I had heard a story about an alcoholic who sees a house burning down. He stands there watching it and the first thing he says is, "I wonder what caused that?" He tries to figure out the reason why it happened. Meanwhile the house burns to ashes and he isn't doing anything to stop the fire. It's the alcoholic's inability to react to reality that enables the walls of denial to remain up so high and stretched so wide.

I could not react to the threat Dan put in front of me. In my mind I pictured myself as he described me: sick, needy, but unable to react, to do something about it. I felt incapable of stopping the progress of the sickness. I was willing to analyze why I was the way I was, but I resisted admitting the actual feelings I was experiencing at the time. Yet I could not accept the future that might await me if I continued denying and blocking my dire need for love. The fear created by the reality of a life confined to a mental institution did not motivate me to get honest with my feelings in any consistent way.

Dan got me thinking, but I still remained unable to share much of my past with the group. I was suffering inside, behind that big grin which I hated now because I wanted to make it go away, but couldn't. It was there, keeping people from reaching my inner soul which needed to be nurtured like a wounded child. I was disappointed with myself because I was so close to breaking down in the group and yet it never happened. I would experience overwhelming frustration and anger from not being able to sit down and deal with the issues which were really eating me up from the inside. I knew they were there and sometimes I could describe in graphic detail the nightmares I had lived through, but I was incapable of allowing myself to experience the painful feelings that should have gone along with them. I had a chance now to dump it all, and yet I could not seriously think about what was bothering me when I was confronted with it! It haunted me when I was unable to do anything about it.

Yet later, after group for instance, we'd be playing volleyball and I 'd say to myself, "I want to dump them now. I want to talk. Now I'm ready. I had my chance to get honest in the group and I didn't so now I have to hurt until next group session." Then group session would roll around the next morning, and strangely enough, that burning desire to spill my guts is gone again, and the grin has returned. The abuse is never discussed; I bury further down.

Sixteen
Individual Therapy

Mr. Sherwood and I met either two or three times a week on an individual basis. I liked having his undivided attention.

In terms of my most obvious personality traits, Mr. Sherwood sized me up pretty quickly, not in a critical way, but rather, in a constructive way. He always confronted me on how I reacted in group. His favorite line began, "Denise, I'm a little concerned. . . ."

So I knew I was due for a confrontation with Mr. Sherwood after the group in which I failed to respond to Dan. He said: "Denise, I'm a little concerned. You know Dan is right. We have been in group for a couple of weeks now and you really haven't shared too much. You share with me in here when we are alone, but you hold back a lot in the group. You know part of recovery is opening up, learning how to trust others. We have to take risks sometimes or we don't grow. What was so funny about what Dan was talking about?"

"Nothing was funny about it. I laugh at everything. I don't understand it either. It just happens automatically. I don't think about it, I don't have any control over it. Sometimes I have to really hold myself back or walk away from serious situations because I feel I am about to laugh inappropriately. Sometimes I really don't want to laugh and I just do it. I don't know what's wrong with me, really. I don't know where the habit came from. I smile if I don't want to and I smile if I do. I don't understand it either."

"Well, how are you feeling when you start to laugh?"

"I usually feel nervous. I feel nervous and unsure. But I can't even limit it to that because I laugh even when I don't feel nervous. I laugh when I am perfectly comfortable and nothing is funny or unusual. But sometimes it seems like I'm very aware of the people around me when I laugh and what they might be feeling. It's sort of eerie, sometimes. And sometimes I think I laugh because I know when people are aware of my presence and that it is affecting them in some way. This inappropriate smiling confuses a lot of people and I don't like that at all. It sort of makes me feel that they're thinking to themselves that I'm a little off the wall, out of touch—when the truth is that I am so very in touch—with *some*thing. It's difficult to explain. It happens all the time. It happened in high school when I knew a teacher was watching me, but she didn't know I knew or when I got into trouble. It happened in the military when I got into trouble. And the laughing always got me into more trouble. The more trouble I got into the more I laughed. I don't know. It makes a whole lot of people angry, especially these military people."

"Do you think maybe it covers up something else you might feel if you didn't laugh, like pain, for instance?" Mr. Sherwood asked.

"I really don't think so because when I smile I'm not always thinking about something painful. Sometimes I'll just smile if someone walks in the room. Or I'll smile if somebody does something that annoys me, something that I really don't think is funny and then the person thinks that I do think it's funny. It's very confusing. Believe me, it disturbs me as much as it disturbs you."

"I think it is very important that you try to understand why you smile, Denise. A way you might begin is by being conscious of when you smile and how you feel when you do it. I see it as an avoidance technique for you. You have a beautiful smile, but it isn't always real."

From that point on it our relationship, every time I smiled Mr. Sherwood said; "You're smiling. Why are you smiling?" Sometimes, I could tell him why, but it didn't stop me from doing it. I came to understand that very often I smiled because it was the only thing I knew how to do. I smiled because I didn't know how to cry. I smiled because I didn't know how to express my anger. I smiled because I was afraid, I smiled because I was not afraid. I smiled because I knew something, I smiled because I didn't know something. There was no end to it. I smiled when I met somebody new. I smiled when I met somebody I already knew. I smiled as I walked down the street alone. I smiled when someone was walking with me. I smiled when things were funny and when things were serious. Smiling seemed like a nice, normal thing to do, but for me it wasn't because it was all I knew. My smile kept others from knowing me and it seemed to be an indication that something was going on with me which I could not articulate.

Mr. Sherwood continued: "Now that we have that as cleared up as it can be for now, let's talk about Dan's question. Why couldn't you come around and answer Dan straightforwardly, with a yes or no answer? You wasted a lot of the group's time beating around the bush. Why couldn't you open up to the group?"

"I just didn't feel like it."

"You know, Denise, there are a lot of things you're going to have to do that you don't feel like doing if you want to get better. Beginning to trust is one of them. If you can't trust in this extremely safe atmosphere, how are you ever going to learn to trust anyone on the outside?

Not everyone out there is going to care, either. You have to meet people half way. Our relationship is very special, but you aren't going to find it in many places. You have to learn to reach out to the rest of the people out there or you'll never grow and you'll continue to be isolated. In order to quit feeling like you are different, like there is something wrong with you, you have to express your feelings and share your experiences. That is the only way other people can identify with you and it will help you to see you are not so unique. You have been through a lot for someone your age, but it's time now for you to start to get rid of the pain. The way to get rid of the pain is to talk it to death. That means opening up in group. No one is going to hurt you in the group. Share with them. Sharing is part of your recovery. If you neglect feeling the hurt now, it will come back at you later on. You really need to get rid of the pain right here while you have the opportunity. I'd like to propose an agreement that you will be willing to open up more in group. What do you think?"

"I can't help it if I just don't feel like sharing. Either I feel like sharing or I don't."

"You think remaining anonymous is going to keep you special or do you think concealing your past keeps you living in it?"

"I just don't feel like sharing. What's wrong with me sharing them with you? Isn't that enough?"

"Unfortunately that's not enough. Everyone else is opening up in group, getting to the core of the pain, but you aren't, Denise. It isn't fair to the others in the group either. Some of them have been through some very painful stuff too. Everybody has to give in some."

"Well, I shared with you some of the stuff."

"You're not hearing me, Denise! I understand that you share with me and I think that you are very good at

154

getting honest with me. All I am saying at this point is that if Dan asks you about something in group, be willing to do your best to answer him rather than avoid him. It can be very frustrating to him and to the rest of the group to allow you to continue to dodge important issues. It is crucial that you talk about things here and now, while you have the opportunity. That is what you are here for, to dump the garbage from the past. Get it off your chest. I am pleased with the progress we've been making in here. Now I'd like to see you stretch it out into the group. What do you think?"

"I think that I could try a little harder, I guess. I don't know. I don't understand why I react like that, so evasive and all."

"Well," Mr. Sherwood said, "you're going through a lot of changes right now and it's not going to be all comfortable. All I ask is that you try and be aware of what you are doing because awareness is always the first step toward changing something. What you ultimately need is to talk your past to death so it no longer causes the pain. It then loses its power over you."

The afternoon after that session I was thinking about the significance of my first session with Mr. Sherwood. It was the first session, when I felt an almost immediate connection to him, which set the mood for our relationship. We talked for a little over an hour and by the end of that period of time we had come to the conclusion that I was searching; and to find what I was searching for, I needed to look elsewhere. Nothing satisfied me. I had a past filled with rich experiences, yet all the satisfaction I gained through my journey was temporary. I was a popular rebel in high school. After high school I went straight off to a good college which I was able to go to because I was fortunate enough to receive funding through the Higher

Educational Opportunity Program. I had been to Europe on a student exchange program during my senior year in college. I studied in London for six months and traveled all over Europe. This did not provide me with lasting satisfaction. I had enough money to meet my needs. This did not seem to relieve me of emptiness. Being with my family hadn't satisfied me. Being away from my family hadn't either. Drinking provided temporary relief, but as time went on the periods of relief became shorter and shorter and the periods of guilt and remorse got longer. So I stopped drinking. I certainly received no immediate relief or satisfaction from that. In fact, that is exactly when I lost my mind more thoroughly.

Life in general did not satisfy my need. Anything and everything that granted me relief and satisfaction had an ending. Every adventure and every retreat, was a temporary solution to a permanent problem. I was repeatedly left with the empty, haunting unfulfilled pit. Yet I realized I was fortunate because, though I was unfulfilled and suffering the pangs of alienation, I was still young and I had gained tremendous wisdom through exhausting all my resources. Some people waste their whole lives seeking other people or material possessions or worldly goods to make them happy. And still they come to the end of their earthly lives only to feel the emptiness and ask once again, "What am I missing? My whole life is almost over and I still don't feel complete. Something is still missing."

And so, at the end of my first session with Mr. Sherwood, we agreed on one thing: that nothing physical or material was going to fill my inner pit which never felt even half filled. I was yearning for something I could not buy or earn in this world: a spiritual life. I never seriously considered that having a spiritual life, whatever that

156

might mean, could in some way be a source of comfort for me during my chaotic and painful emotional state. I read about God in Catholic religion class, but that God lived in the textbook, like all those other wonderful characters I read about in books but never experienced as part of my life.

I thought I was in the rehab because I was losing my mind. I was. I realized I no longer could go on the way I was, yet I did not get what they said all the time in AA meetings about "surrendering my will to a power greater than myself." But I was told this again and again and I was told that until I did this, I would be in absolute misery. However, as simple a solution as surrendering my will to God appeared to be, it was not the painless solution I was still intent on finding. And it certainly didn't mean my long-nurtured dysfunctional way of existing was going to suddenly disappear. I occasionally found myself uttering under my breath: Perhaps God's will is for me to work through the pain and quit looking for a quick and easy way out. Or perhaps I was expected to accept my lousy life?

So Mr. Sherwood and I decided that what I was searching for was of the spiritual realm. I had never, in all sincerity, turned to God for help in any consistent way. It seemed silly to turn to a God whom I could not see or hear. And how was I to trust a God who had me on the road to hell?

Mr. Sherwood believed in the Catholic God and he believed that my spirit was open to the notion of establishing a relationship with a God, some God. We began to speak of God openly and often enough so that Mr. Sherwood was able to convey to me that I didn't have to solve all my problems alone. He assured me that if I learned to trust God with my problems, they wouldn't be such a tremendous burden and I would learn to handle them with His assistance. Mr. Sherwood was a Catholic which was, technically, my religion at that time. I did not know that just because I was raised Catholic it meant I had to stay a Catholic forever. No one ever told me that I had a choice, that I could choose any religion I wanted to or that I could decide to choose not to have a religion at all.

But at the time I was in treatment with Mr. Sherwood, familiarity with Catholicism was something we had in common and that helped our relationship as well. He understood some of the problems the Catholic encounters if he/she comes around and begins to question what is present or lacking from her faith. We began discussing the difference between going to church and practicing my faith. At that time I thought that if I went to church I was practicing my faith and after not being able to figure out why I was so empty after going to church for so many years, I quit going to church.

Mr. Sherwood had the quality a therapist needs, the ability to show compassion without feeling sorry for his patient. He had no pity for me, though I attempted to evoke it at times. As we began clearing up the wreckage of my past, I became aware that I was a prime target for the disease of alcoholism and many other mental illnesses. I explained to Mr. Sherwood, "I really thought I was crazy when I was a kid because people always told me I was. Even the neighbors who heard me screaming at the top of my lungs thought I was nuts. I always felt a bit different from other kids, even from my own brothers and sisters. I survived, you know—I mean I learned how to make my way in this world, how to survive by stuffing feelings and muddling along, sometimes laughing, sometimes crying, but never knowing why and always knowing in the back of my mind that I wasn't normal—that I was crazy and that one night my mother's threats to call the police and have them take me away to an institution would really happen. I knew one night she would do it because she'd be tired and angry. And you know something? I never could enjoy those ice-cream cones I screamed so loudly for. Once I got my quarter and darted out of the apartment fast enough so my mother couldn't grab me and beat the shit out of me, I'd get downstairs to the ice-cream truck and I was ridden with guilt asking the Good Humor man for my ice cream. My eyes were all puffy and red and I was so embarrassed 'cause I thought he knew. I would snatch my ice cream real quick and run to the alleyway and eat it by myself in the corner."

Mr. Sherwood had been listening intently. Now he asked, "Denise, I never saw you cry, not in group or in here. Do you ever cry?"

I never answered. I just sat lost in my memories. And then something came over me. I didn't feel like crying. I felt like being closer to Mr. Sherwood, like curling up in his lap and letting him rock me back and forth while I rested my head on his shoulder. I had felt so warm inside because someone had listened to me talk about a painful memory. I was experiencing his being there for me and nothing could ever have been more comforting to me than that. I never mourned over my lost childhood. I supposed now that I never mourned it because there was no one there for me in the same way Mr. Sherwood had just been there for me. I was silent and Mr. Sherwood and I sat in the silence for a while. But I didn't cry. I always cried alone.

I had a hard time getting up out of my seat when that session was over. I wanted more of what I had just experienced with Mr. Sherwood and I never wanted it to end. I suppose I needed a great deal more of it, otherwise I would not have craved it so much. . . .

Well, the craving for a person who could give me what Mr. Sherwood had given me in that five minutes was soon to become what I would pursue for many, many years. The process of my pursuit felt similar to the way in which I pursued alcohol once I began to drink. Instead of finding a bottle to ease my pain, I would find a person. And the same vicious cycle would set in. The more I got, the more frightened I became. The more frightened I became, the more I needed to calm the fear and soothe my emotions. It would be out of control just as my need for alcohol got out of control. The feelings of desperation would all be the same, even worse because it would be a specific human being I needed to swallow and not just any old bottle of wine. The feeling that I was going to die without would all feel very familiar to me.

Mr. Sherwood and I talked about everything from my childhood to spirituality to the military and to anything else that came up. During the season which Catholics call Lent, I was in the rehab. I decided to go to mass one afternoon. To my surprise I found Mr. Sherwood at mass when I got there, so we sat together in the hospital chapel. Occasionally on the weekends, we'd go on a bicycling tour with the chaplain from the hospital. We'd ride all around Germany—over thirty miles! Once on the bike tour we stopped at a crosswalk and Mr. Sherwood ran over my toes by accident with his front tire and I screamed out, "Hey, watch it! My toes have feelings too!"

I was really reaching out to Mr. Sherwood and he was meeting me more than halfway. I was experiencing myself in life other than saturated with depression, isolation, and joylessness. It was time to grow and Mr. Sherwood was there as my guide. Only I turned him into my God, and so, the next painful lesson was about to be learned. That lesson included the terrible, but necessary, experience of coming to understand that Mr. Sherwood was a human being just like myself and he had no crystal ball into which he could look and see the answers to all life's problems. I knew this intellectually, but the needy child in me wanted Mr. Sherwood to be the "perfect one." Children initially believe their parents are all-knowing; it is only through the passage of time that they come to understand differently.

My intellect and my emotions never balanced out. Always, what I knew intellectually was light years away from what I felt emotionally. And so it was no wonder that for a very long time, I questioned my sanity. With all the things I could do with my intellect, with all the understanding and knowledge I could gather about my condition, I could not get my intellect to control my emotions. It was like my young wounded soul was fighting my molded intellect for freedom, and because of the strength and persistence of my wounded soul, it beat my intellect in this struggle , almost every time. Thus, I presented as unstable, unpredictable, impulsive, challenging to authority and as possessing a Borderline Personality Disorder.

Seventeen
Breaking the Ties

The process of therapeutic change was, predictably, too heavily wrapped up in the time I spent with Mr. Sherwood. I developed what is known as a regressive attachment and then went through some horrendous pain trying to let go of him. The fear of abandonment was torturous. I couldn't detach because detaching felt like I was losing everything: my progress, my recovery, myself. I was losing the person who had enabled me to experience comfort. I was attached to the physical Mr. Sherwood, Mr. Sherwood in body and flesh, just as a baby is attached to her mother during infancy. Separation from him was the inevitable reality, but a part of me wanted to cling tightly to someone I could see and I knew cared about me because I didn't have the strength to take care of myself. I was not ready to separate. I did not have enough time to go through the developmental stage of attachment which I needed to go through before I moved on to separation/individuation, the next stage of development.

Mr. Sherwood could not have possibly kept up with my demands for his time and energy, even if I had been able to stay in treatment with him. My need was insatiable. One afternoon while I was in treatment I asked Mr. Sherwood if he would be going on the bicycle ride the coming weekend and he said he had other plans. My reaction was: *He made other plans and isn't going to be with me! Fuck him! I don't need him! He doesn't give a shit about me anyway!*

I felt that way every time Mr. Sherwood had "other plans" and I carried that feeling with me after I left treatment. I felt not only anger and resentment, but also a deep hurt and a fear of losing Mr. Sherwood and not being able to live satisfied without him. This fear of abandonment I would spend many years in therapy working through. It was as much an illness, in and of itself, as my alcoholism, and it was the driving force behind my unhappiness, my emptiness, and my self-destructive behavior. I had no idea how bad it was really going to get. My life as an independent adult was not going to be realized at the age society deemed it appropriate. Adulthood with all its responsibilities was on hold for me because I had to grow into that being.

I did eventually open up somewhat in group, but it was still much easier for me to do so in private with Mr. Sherwood. I made great progress in individual therapy and not so much in group therapy. I was too accustomed to playing the savior. I rationalized that I was in group to save the other poor souls who had it so much worse than I did.

The six weeks were up and my time to leave treatment arrived. I had to get up in front of a group of about 150 people, most of them military, and tell them what my rehab experience had been like. I had never before stood in front of a group of people and felt comfortable with myself. I didn't feel comfortable this day either, but something was different. This time I had something to share and I believed in what I had to share. I was speaking from real experience, real pain, real frustration, real growth, and real joy. I was speaking from the heart, not merely reading lines off a piece of paper or mumbling some words that I heard someone else say somewhere along the line. I was not acting or pretending to know something I was expected to know, but actually had no clue about.

My commander, Lt. Sharples, was not at my completion ceremony. I hadn't seen her at all during my six weeks in treatment. That wasn't unusual. When soldiers went away for treatment, there wasn't too much contact with the commanders until it was time for them to return to the unit. But it was so difficult for me to accept that she was unable to be there for me on my last day that I convinced myself that she really was there and I just couldn't see her. I believed I would have been discharged or shipped off to the Medical Center in Washington, D.C. if it weren't for Lt. Sharples. I had also grown attached to Lt. Sharples and so to protect myself from the hurt caused by her absence, I pretended and truly believed that she was there. The truth was that she was at another soldier's graduation from a Platoon Leadership Development course. Her friend, Lt. Commton, was at my completion ceremony with a few other people whom I didn't recognize.

While I was in treatment we had to go to AA meetings every Monday, Wednesday, and Friday nights. The meetings were right in the treatment center and I had grown close to quite a few people there and they had come to the ceremony to hear me speak. My sponsor was a soldier too, sober about three years. She had gone through the treatment center three years earlier and her story was another example of the miracles that transpire in sobriety. AA was as vital a part of my recovery as my relationship with Mr. Sherwood was. I wasn't thinking so far ahead because the thought of living without Mr. Sherwood was too overwhelming to consider, but the reality was that Mr. Sherwood would not always be with me. Alcoholics Anonymous would be. The members of Alcoholics

Anonymous promised me I would not have to struggle alone anymore. Wherever I was to go in this world, AA would be there. This was true, but it was also true that Alcoholics Anonymous could not fill that empty pit either. It helped me to not pick up a drink, though it did not help me with my major depression which came later on in sobriety. The longer I remained sober, the more depressed I became. If Mr. Sherwood was around then, even his presence would not have been enough to lift me out of the depression I sank into. I just stopped caring about everything, even myself. I became quite a scare to my family and friends when my outward appearance began to match my inner hopelessness. One of my sisters saw me one afternoon and she angrily asked me why I was dressed like a homeless person. She believed I was dressing inappropriately just to be defiant and to be an embarrassment to my family.

The people I met in Alcoholics Anonymous had experienced incredible pain before they arrived on the doorstep of these rooms and they didn't think twice about sharing their pain with me. They told me I wasn't crazy and in the beginning I needed to hear that constantly just to keep myself alive to wake up for the next day. For a while that was enough to keep me hanging on. And some of the stories I heard in AA meetings left me with hope. One night I listened to a man share about how he had driven drunk and killed a six-year-old boy crossing the street. Another man had awakened in jail and couldn't remember what he had done or how he'd gotten there. One woman spoke of her utter loneliness and how she needed the booze to curb her lonely feelings and then found herself growing lonelier with the opening of each bottle. She reminded me of my mother in her later years of drinking. She drank alone and I know she was very lonely and alone. A girl about my age shared about how she had gotten drunk to get the courage to kill herself. She had jumped off a bridge and, miraculously, lived. All these people were in a room with me and they seemed to be learning how to come to terms with their pasts. For the first time in their lives, they were succeeding in finding peace and serenity. It was through these meetings that I learned that I was sick from years of sick thinking and sick drinking and that while I was not going to get better overnight, I could eventually recover if I didn't resort to alcohol. If I picked up alcohol again I would not be able to change the negative attitudes I nurtured or the maladaptive patterns I'd established over many years. The true struggle was for the freedom from self-inflicted oppression.

I was the last in my group to speak. I was tremulous walking up to the podium, dressed in my dress greens and high heels. I walked to the center of the stage in front of the podium, stopped, looked up at the crowd of people in the stands and said, very fast and without stopping to take a breath in between words:

"My name's Denise Marie Patricia Ranaghan and I'm an Irish Catholic alcoholic.

They all laughed. Everybody else had said, My name is Peggy and I'm an alcoholic, or Bob, alcoholic—very short and concise statements. I didn't mean to be funny. I was deadly serious and I was too petrified and too stiff to laugh at my own funniness. I was in a very serious mood. I had a message to share. I went on when the laughing slowed down.

"You know you don't have to be Irish to be an alcoholic. You don't have to be Catholic to be an alcoholic. The disease claims all races and nationalities. It destroys families by the thousands. It is not picky about its victims

[I looked over at all my friends from the rehab and they were shaking their heads up and down very seriously]. I'd like to try something with you. I'm going to count to three and when I say three I want everyone to turn around and say hello to the person sitting behind you. One . . . two . . . three!"

The room got very noisy for a few seconds, noisy with those people who greeted each other and smiled, and those who were still searching for the person behind them who had already turned around. It was supposed to work that way because everybody would turn around at the same time, nobody would have anybody to say hello to and they might experience the feeling of aloneness in this smallest way when they were expecting to feel acknowledged and welcomed. But people reached out, some in a panic, and made contact. They tapped each other on the back in a desperate attempt to find each other. Some laughed impulsively when that probably would not have been the immediate response to the disappointment of having no one to say hello to. They would not tolerate, not even for a moment, an uncomfortable feeling.

Next I said, "Okay, now I want you to do that to me. I want you to count to three and I will do the same."

I walked over to the edge of the platform so when I turned around there was nothing but an empty basketball court behind me. They counted for me and on three I turned around and screamed, "Hello!" My voice echoed through the whole roller rink. I turned back around to the people in the bleachers and I said to them, almost in tears and my voice shaking with sincerity, "All my life I turned out there (I pointed back to the empty space behind me)! All my life I turned where there were no people because I never truly experienced connecting with anyone. I ran and hid from people and shouted into the emptiness. And when I got no response from the empty arenas, it confirmed my belief that no one could hear me, no one wanted to hear me. I never trusted a soul. I never reached out to other people. I always sat in dingy hallways and smelly alleyways, shouting hello into the empty bottles of wine I polished off by myself, not even shared with a drinking buddy. In the rehab I learned to trust again. I learned that my answers are not out there in the empty places. The answers are right here inside you and me. I see now that God works through people just like you and me."

I was finished. I started walking over to my seat and the people started clapping for me and then I turned around because I wanted to do one more thing: "Oh, wait a minute. One more thing. Could everybody please stand up. Thank you. I don't ever want to stand alone again!" And that was the end of the ceremony.

I never felt so euphoric in my life. People came up to hug me, people I didn't even know. Everybody was grabbing me and congratulating me. My friend David was there too, and he came up to me and we stared into each other's eyes for a few seconds as we held one another. We were both smiling with joy and then a sort of seriousness came over us and he said, "I gotta go. My wife's waiting in the car. Keep in touch, will ya?"

"You know I will," I said.

The last person to come up to me was Mr. Sherwood. He came up, calm as always, but with such a proud smile on his face, a smile I interpreted as, "I knew you were something special and I know you're going to make it." We hugged each other and I wished I could have held onto him forever. I wasn't fully feeling my need for Mr. Sherwood. I was too elated. This elated feeling I would come to know well in the years ahead. Part of my work during recovery would have to do with taming these elated feelings in an effort to gain some control; control over how much of my terrific feelings and how much of my lousy feelings, I would display in public. But as for Mr. Sherwood, in this particular moment of jubilation my need for him was a manageable feeling which lingered within me. Unfortunately, the intensity of my need for him was to return to haunt me long after treatment at the Residential Treatment Facility was finished.

The letting-go part was not easy. Besides looking toward Mr. Sherwood as a father figure, I had sexual feelings toward him too. I had a fantasy that one day we were going to marry and live a wonderful life together in love. But the part of me that knew that would never happen was very depressed and sad. I yearned for our relationship to be something more than it was, something it never would be. He did remain my counselor when I got out of treatment. He didn't have to. It wasn't a formal arrangement. I just went and talked to him whenever something came up and I needed help. Our relationship and his willingness to continue to see me was what helped me survive in the military environment for as long as I did.

I left the treatment center that afternoon flying high in the cotton clouds. Nothing could harm me. I was on top of the world. Everything was perfect for the moment. I didn't have to go to work that day because it was late afternoon by the time I got back to the unit. I went to my barracks room and began to unpack my army duffle bag.

Once I got back to my room, the transformation began. I don't even know if "transformation" is the accurate word to use to describe what happened to me. Transformation implies a process. I was not aware of a process going on. It was more like an instantaneous emotional swing from a feeling of having triumphed over life itself to

169

a feeling of having sunk into the depths of despair about having to live in a world I hated. The swing was from life to death, from hope to despair. Suddenly, I was alone and afraid and wondered what the hell to do with myself. It was like I needed all those people who were at the closing ceremony, but they had vanished.

How could I feel so wonderful one minute and so utterly insecure the next? "Just unpack," I said to myself. *And then what? I don't want to be here. I'm on my own.* I thought as I sat hunched over on the edge of my bed with the tears streaming down my cheeks. I had been pushed out of the womb, the warm, nurturing caring environment at the RTF. *I miss my buddies from the RTF. They are scattered all over Germany, some of them as much as four hours away.*

My mind raced, searching for a solution as I sat and stared at my luggage on the floor in front of me. As I called on my intellect for a solution one popped into my head: "I'll unpack and go to the AA meeting at the RTF at 7:30 P.M. Of course! That's what I've been doing all along. I will go to a meeting and a few of the friends I met in the program will be there. I can talk about how I feel."

I managed to finish unpacking. I passed the rest of the afternoon writing in my journal and then went to the meeting. I hadn't seen my roommate since I'd been back. I guessed she was out and about. It was Friday.

Eighteen
Back to Reality

During the first months out of treatment I had few problems. I had a new outlook on life and felt like a new person. I was positive, motivated to do my duties as a soldier, and always volunteering for every extra duty that came up. I remembered to wear my dog tags to formation and I ironed my uniform. I also did not condemn myself if I wasn't perfect. It was okay that one boot was shinier than the other, or that I stopped scrubbing the sinks in the bathroom before my arm was sore. I did what I could and I let it go at that. I didn't obsess about perfection. If it wasn't good enough, I would be told and then I'd do it over again. If not, what's the big deal about having one shiny boot and one not-as-shiny boot?

I liked myself. I was confident, overflowing with energy and joy. Life was a beautiful gift and it was not to be taken so seriously. And it was okay to make mistakes. I even thought it was alright to ask for a pass every once in a while and if I didn't get it, well at least I asked. I was so positive that it confused people. If they thought there was something wrong with me before, now they were irrevocably convinced. I didn't see anything when I was on my cloud, except joyful ecstasy. Life was a bowl of pitless cherries. It was exciting to be so totally uninhibited and fearless. But it didn't last.

I didn't understand, at first, why people were actually angry with me. They were always making faces about me and snickering behind my back, mostly the girls, but I was too happy and free to waste time analyzing other people's reactions to me. I remained unaffected in my state of joyful bliss and I think this made people even angrier.

I did eventually begin to notice and feel bothered by the general lack of respect, the blatant disregard toward my personhood. For instance, once when my roommate flung the door wide open while I was changing clothes and I brought it to her attention that I would appreciate it if she would be more aware of when I was clothed and when I wasn't, because I didn't want the whole barracks to see me naked, she became angry and defensive: "Nobody was there! It's not like anyone was outside the door! What do you expect from me? Am I supposed to change the way I live now that you're out of the hospital?"

"No," I answered. "I would just appreciate it if you could be a little more considerate, and if you have to leave the room while I'm changing, let me know and I'll get behind the locker."

She puffed her way out the door, obviously enraged that I felt I had rights. Before I went into the hospital I didn't demand consideration from anyone so, of course, no one expected me to be any different now. It was painful just learning how to stand up for myself. Sometimes I felt like I owed it to myself to ask for consideration. Others resented it. My roommate, who had been there for me while I was ill, was unwilling to stand by me when I was getting well. As long as I was sick and needy I was a threat to no one, but when I started to recover and consider myself worthy of the time of day, many people who had been "nice" to me before, became very angry with me. I began to sense that people had been respectful to me, not because they really thought me worthwhile, but because they either pitied me or because they felt more secure about themselves believing I was a sick person.

It was difficult trying to express how I felt about things. I also didn't have the choice of who my supervisor would be. When our personalities clashed I was the one who had to submit all the time. Few people trusted me because my history spoke for itself. I had been in the unit for five months and I had already made it to the psychiatric ward and the alcohol rehab center. Because others and myself—though less now than before—perceived these trips as proof of my weak character, a large part of me was eager to clear the slate, to fix everything, to be understood and free of the derogatory labels that psychiatric patients often get pinned with.

I felt tremendous pressure to prove myself. In my mind, the whole unit knew I had had some problems and in the military, having some problems is considered weak. If you don't resolve your own problems and play the "I am invincible" game, then others either avoid you or scapegoat you. I was avoided by some and scapegoated by others. My childish, carefree attitude, which naturally emerged as a result of the nurturing environment of the treatment facility, was not acceptable in the military. It felt really beautiful to experience the bliss that only a child could feel when expressing him/herself. For the first time in my life I was so carefree and uninhibited.

But children are also self-centered. They live in their own little worlds, interested only in their limited view, unable to comprehend the whole picture. I was preoccupied with my own needs and feelings. Before now I had been too busy protecting myself, running away, trying to get other people's attention or worrying about other people's responses. Now here I was, getting in touch with the child inside me, learning about my individual identity, but I was in a group-oriented environment. A child

173

doesn't belong in the military. A child gets crushed in the military.

As my awareness of my environment too quickly grew, so did my frustration. In my state of self-absorption, I assumed that just as I was sober and learning so many new things, so was everybody else. But my supervisor, for instance, was a blatant alcoholic who, when she got angry, became abusive to me in a way too reminiscent of my mother. She reminded me of an old tape of my mother criticizing me, one which ran through my head and went something like this: *You can't do anything right. You're crazy. You really are crazy. You should be in a looney bin. You'll never get anywhere in life. You are really nuts.*

After enough negative reinforcement from my supervisor, I began to question my competence again. That's when I realized that twenty-two years of low self-esteem could not be erased with six weeks of treatment. My awareness had increased, and I had received my first taste of freedom and love, but the bad feelings would take years to work through.

Working under SFC (Sergeant First Class) Hardy, my supervisor, I spent most of my counted minutes trying to tame the fierce rage that was rising within me. SFC Hardy stopped giving me work to do. She assumed I would make things worse and since she assumed this, the little work she did give me, I managed poorly. She magnified all my small mistakes, like a typo or an erasure. Despite my anger at her rejection of me, I found myself constantly trying hard not to make a mistake. In doing so, I doubled my errors. I was a bundle of nerves, always trying to prove my usefulness to someone who, no matter what I did, found fault with me. As SFC Hardy continued to pick me apart, she simultaneously reassured herself of my incompetence. And me—what happened to all that self-esteem, that spirit, that confidence I had built up? How disappointing to leave such a safe nurturing environment, and have to return to one so filled with constant criticism and devaluation. How utterly shattered I felt before I stopped caring, faded into the woodwork, and lost my hope . . . again.

I craved a supportive environment, something I would never have at 596th. Having to take orders from some of the most dishonest people I ran into assured me of that. One sergeant summed it up quite accurately when he told me: "Look, anyone can make it in the army. You just have to cover your own ass. You can be the greatest slimebag in the world, but if you know how to cover your own ass, you'll make it in the military." I never found a statement to be so thoroughly true. Many soldiers were taught that their survival was dependent upon their appearance and to appear perfect they had to acquire the ability to clear their names of everything from the smallest, most understandable mistake to the greater more significant wrongdoings. Whether what they did was right or wrong didn't matter so long as they didn't get caught. Everything from rape, to theft, to bribery, to daily verbal abuse went on right under my nose, and I was powerless over it all, especially as a low-ranking soldier, not to mention a former mental patient.

For my part I had my own share of mistakes, but I paid for them because I wasn't quite good enough, or interested enough, in "covering my own ass." Somehow I moved into this state of cash register honesty about everything I said and did. I felt compelled to be this way for the sake of my recovery so when I accidentally left the office one day with Lt. Sharples's pencil, I went back with it and explained that I had accidentally walked off with it and was terribly sorry. She rolled her eyes and said: "Keep the pencil, Ranaghan."

I was aching for the freedom to be me, but it was hard to be myself in the army without serious consequences. All I talked about and thought about was recovery. All my fellow soldiers talked about and thought about was the great party last night, or who was getting promoted. My peers did not respond to me or even listen to me when I spoke. It was as if I was totally invisible. And I cared so little about promotions that I managed to get demoted. For a few months I had walked around with the "Specialist" symbol pinned on my military jacket, more because the time had come to promote me than because anyone thought I had earned it. A few months after the promotion a new commander came to our unit and had me demoted within two months of her arrival. I was to leave the military with the same rank I had entered it with, Private First Class.

I went to aftercare once a week at the Community Counseling Center. It offered group therapy for people who were going into treatment and people who had just gotten out. I found it frustrating at times because the people going into treatment were struggling with denial, most not even believing they were alcoholics, while the people just out of treatment were struggling with problems of readjustment to their units. Sometimes I felt so frustrated with the people denying their disease because I could see their denial so easily. It had taken me eight years to give up drinking for good, and now I was frustrated with others who were denying the "obvious." But the group gave me an outlet, a place to turn if things became overwhelming. I attended the group religiously on Tuesday afternoons. If it did nothing else, it got me away from my unit. It never did measure up to the group I had

had in treatment with Dan and Mr. Sherwood because the counselors in this outpatient treatment were comparatively inexperienced and wishy-washy, and that left me with a very lonely feeling inside.

For a while I learned how to survive by tuning out my environment rather than striving to control it. I coped by busying myself with extra responsibilities in the unit, pursuits I enjoyed. I managed to become known as the battalion photographer, a job I discovered for myself and followed through by myself. It kept me occupied and feeling useful. I was given a great deal of freedom on the job because SFC Hardy refused to assign me any work other than taking the garbage to the dumpster at 5 o'clock. So I became my own boss. I began working on a battalion newsletter so I'd have something to do with all the pictures I took and developed. I used the darkroom down the hall to develop my film and when I was stuck in the office I worked on typing the newsletter.

However, as time passed, it became more and more evident that this military environment was not for me, that I was a round circle trying to fit into a square peg. The military did not welcome the kind of struggle and search for identity I now needed to undertake. I was torn between the commitment I had made to the military and my personal need to get out. The inner conflict had to do with my treatment at the rehab facility which I never would have received without Lt. Sharples's help, and Lt. Sharples was part of the system. I could not separate the individual, Lt. Sharples, from the system, the army, in which she played a role. As a result I felt indebted to both. I was anxious to give back some of what I had received from the service.

Eventually I realized I needed to repay one caring human being, not the whole system. I wanted to repay Lt.

Sharples for her help by being the ideal soldier. I wanted to prove myself and let her know how much I appreciated her kind patience. But fate stepped in the way.

Before long, the change of command rolled around and Lt. Sharples was on her way out, to serve a tour of duty in the States. With her departure my world caved in. She had been such a staunch source of encouragement for me. My admiration for her was undying and as long as she was commander, I had the will to at least act my part.

But her time was up, and shortly after she left, Sergeant Major Hooker was retiring and returning to the States. He was the Battalion Command Sergeant Major whose office was across the hall from mine. He had also been a significant source of encouragement for me; they were the only two people with whom I had established relationships based on understanding and trust, not fear. They also valued my work, my photography and the newsletter I put out monthly. A few months after Sergeant Major Hooker left for the States, I received a letter from him with a clipping from his hometown newspaper. It was a story on Sergeant Major Hooker, and the picture above the story was a photo I had taken of him in his office. It was a picture which I shot and then developed myself. Sergeant Major Hooker was a large, well-built black man who had gained some weight with age. He thanked me for taking the picture (which showed him only from his chest up). He was sitting with his elbows stretched in opposite directions across the top of his desk while he interlocked his fingers and rested them on the surface in front of him. Sergeant Major Hooker had a beautiful smile which he displayed in this picture. But even more than all of this, he liked me, even if he didn't totally understand me. He found me amusing; yet I never felt he was laughing at me, because I found myself amusing also when I was in his presence. He brought out a more light-hearted side of me which did not emerge with very many people I encountered in the military.

And Sergeant Major Hooker did not assume I was stupid because of my history in the military. What he said to me one day was, "You know something, Ranaghan? There's something about you. I don't understand it. You're okay. You're right on top of things. And yet, every once in a while you just go off the wall. You lose it. Other than that, you're right on the money."

Sergeant Major Hooker was referring to some angry outbursts which I had periodically when I just couldn't hold it all in anymore. My binges of rage were usually directed at someone who worked in the office with me and acted as if I was invisible.

Once Lt. Sharples and Sergeant Major Hooker had gone, it seemed I couldn't be a soldier anymore. I understood, clearly, that I had not been struggling to make it for myself. I was only trying to show the people who believed in me that their efforts were not in vain, in much the same way a child wants to impress her parents and make them proud. I wanted them to know, I was truly grateful to them for respecting me as a person. Their departures had a final devastating effect on my performance as a soldier.

The new leaders in my unit didn't know exactly what to do with me. I confused a number of them and angered many more. I sometimes either challenged orders or went to the other extreme and followed orders so literally that I ridiculed the system. For instance an officer said to me: "Stand there in the position of attention and don't you say a word. Do you understand me, Private?" I would do what I was told and so, feel obligated not to respond to his/her question, for then I would be disobeying the order not to speak.

Toward the end of my tour, I was moved four times to four different offices. I seemed to be the one who was moved whenever there was a need. I was well aware that I was the first one chosen for a new duty because the people in charge believed that whatever I was doing was not so significant that it couldn't be left undone. The only reason I really resented being moved around so much was because it took me away from working on the newsletter and so I had to drop it altogether. I had hoped to expand the newsletter and get more people involved in it so that it would improve and become more professional and informative over time. I had hoped to make a significant contribution to the unit by using my writing in this way.

It was very self-defeating for me to force myself to like my job and my position in the army. The more I told myself. "You *should* be doing a better job . . . you *should* be more interested in what you're doing . . . you *should* be grateful and proud to be here," the worse I felt about myself. I began to wonder again what was wrong with me. I thought, *Why am I so unmotivated to work and to live? Why is this job so unimportant to me? Why am I so lazy?*

I had duty in the Installation Coordinator's office for a while, typing and answering phones, and, occasionally, working outside on the installation, helping with clean-up or special duty. At Christmas time a huge tree was decorated in the center of the Kaserne. Everyone wanted to decorate it, but no one wanted to *un*-decorate it. I spent a day in January un-decorating it by myself. I felt terribly cold and lonely, as the holidays always hit me especially hard anyway.

When I was no longer needed in the Installation Coordinator's office, I was moved back to the orderly room in the battalion. After a few weeks there I was transferred to work in the gym for a few weeks. While I was working in the gym I was expected to tolerate more verbal abuse, and on rare occasions, physical abuse. One weightlifter came in the gym and reached his huge hand through the window and into my office to pick up the telephone. When I told him the phone could be used by him only for emergencies, he said he used the phone all the time. I then asked him who he was. He just kept dialing. Then I asked him if he could tell me who he was calling on my phone. He ignored me. I next asked him to please put the telephone down. He told me to "fuck off." So I pushed the button and disconnected his call. He was furious. Without even thinking for a split second, he slammed the phone down and pushed me backward. He was so strong that I lost my balance, fell backward and slammed into the metal wall locker behind me.

Now it was my turn to react without thinking. I started screaming. "He pushed me! That motherfucker *pushed me into the locker!*" I ran over to him and screamed in his face, "You think you can get away with that! You think you're gonna get away with that, you fucking pig?"

And he said to me in a voice which actually sounded a little frightened, "I didn't do anything. You have no witnesses."

I ran around the gym looking for the manager. I found him in the handball court engaged in an intense game. I opened the door to the court and as soon as he saw my face, he stopped playing. I told him what happened. I was hysterical because I was so shocked. The manager came out and he went over to talk to the offender who denied the whole thing. There was nothing the manager could do. But he said if I wanted to file a report I could go over to the military police station.

I ran across the grass from the gym to the military police station, which was the battalion I worked for, and I filed a complaint. The officers saw how shook up I was, so they told me to be calm and write down everything that happened. I did that and then the police went over to the gym and asked the manager where this guy was. The MPs then went into the men's locker room and dragged the offender out of the sauna. They took him to the station and held him only long enough until he finished documenting his denial of the incident. Then they had to let him go because I had no witnesses. All I had as proof was what I found on my chest the next morning in the shower: a large bruise just above my breasts. And that they would say, could have been from anything.

While working in the gym I often found it necessary to stand my ground. Many soldiers who came to use the gym were not used to following the rules and they were even less used to having a woman remind them of what those rules were. I was the only woman who worked in the gym.

After enough noise at the gym, I was sent back to the orderly room for the last few weeks of my stay at the 596th. I worked in the gym only occasionally, when they had no choice because they had nobody else. Mr. Sherwood was surprised I survived as long as I did in the military. So was I. I could have saved myself some pain if I had been discharged a little earlier. But the military did serve a purpose in my life. I came to terms with my alcoholism and my mental illness, and I found one more occupation in life which I was not suited for.

I had a few months of service left and I had accumulated 30 days leave. I anxiously looked forward to 30 glorious days of freedom: no uniform to wear, nobody telling me what to do, where to be or when to be there. I planned to go home and spend the majority of my days with my family at a beach house which my sister had rented for the summer. However, what I had planned for my vacation was different from what actually took place. I did spend time with my family. Some of it was at the beach, but some of it was at the hospital where my mother was admitted for treatment for alcoholism.

Nineteen
Family Therapy

Despite my new commander's doubts and suspicions about allowing me to return to New York for my leave, I did go, and instead of spending thirty days there, I spent three months. I did not plan the extended stay, but Lt. Kinderson believed otherwise. She was aware that I was not happy with the military and that I was not committed to the unit the way I had been when Lt. Sharples was in command. She took my stay in New York as a personal, premeditated attack against her authority, which I must admit, did not bother me in the least. In fact, I took pleasure in imagining her thought process.

Upon returning home, I realized my family was in trouble. My mother was deeply trapped within her disease. She wasn't the worst I had ever seen her, but she was quickly self-destructing. She had reverted to screaming throughout the night and blacking out. Her weekends were the worst because on the weekend she didn't even have to get up for work so she'd drink throughout the night and sleep the whole next day. Her job was the only thing she lived for, the only piece of evidence she could present to justify her health and well-being. Most alcoholics have some sort of refuge, something they can hang onto which is of utmost importance to them and which they use as "proof" that they don't have the disease of alcoholism. Mom would always say, "Well I have a job. I get up every morning for it and I'm never late and I never miss a day." What she really was saying was, "I'm not an alcoholic because I can hold my job and I'm the best worker they have."

So she'd get home from work in the evenings and she'd sit down and do her crossword puzzle, complaining all the while that the house was a mess, and she shouldn't have to work all day and then come home to this "shit house": "After all, I can't do everything. I work all day! What do you think I am?"

So my older sister would cook dinner, and ask others to help with the dishes and help sweep the floor while Ma buried her angry head in the crossword puzzle. It was after dinner that she'd start sneaking her drinks. We all knew because she would leave every few minutes and go into her bedroom and close the door and then come back out and sit down to do her crossword puzzles again and little by little, she'd start to become more talkative. And then her trips to her bedroom would become more frequent, her eyes would start to glow, her face would droop and she'd be very interested in engaging in conversation with us. All of a sudden, the mother wanted to talk, the mother who buried her head in her puzzles, complained her way through dinner and was dreadfully irritable and stressed just an hour ago. Then after talking for a little while, and showing signs of possessing a sense of humor about life, she transformed, before our eyes, into a rageful, vengeful, spiteful monster, ready to fight, physically and verbally, whatever it took. All her drinking bouts ended in arguments and her yelling about her job and her lousy, lonely life. In the early years her benders ended in beatings and fist fights. As the years passed and we children grew too big and strong to abuse, her abuse became mainly verbal threats and flying objects, which might or might not have hit our heads, depending on the time of the evening and the amount of alcohol consumed.

185

I had written to my family from Germany and told them I was an alcoholic and in AA. I didn't tell them of my psychiatric hospitalization; that was too humiliating and seemed much less socially acceptable. But before I left Germany, my friends in AA sent me off with some valuable advice. They warned me not to try to fix the world, not to try to get my family sober, but only to concentrate on keeping myself sober one day at a time. They warned me that when you are recovering from this disease it is vital to keep a distance, for a while, from the family you got sick from and with. I had another idea in mind, though, and no warnings, however wise, were going to change that. I was going home and I felt called upon to do something for my family, though I did not know exactly what.

My mother was about to take a vacation as I arrived home. I boldly took that as an opportunity to go to her job and talk with her supervisor. Her supervisor turned out to be very supportive, though shocked: "Not Barbara. A drinking problem? Are you kidding? She's the best worker we have. We all love her." Despite the conflict between what Louise saw and what was reality about my mother, she was willing to participate in an intervention if I worked out a plan. In fact she was glad to do it. She shared with me about how her own father had died of alcoholism and she had always felt there must have been something she could have done about it.

I journeyed onward to a place a priest recommended, which trained families to plan interventions. I didn't really want to waste money I didn't have on intervention training so, instead, I bought their book and trained myself. I then passed the book on to each family member who would be participating in the intervention and pointed out the chapters they would need to read in order to carry out their role in the intervention. The intervention would include all but one of my siblings, and my mother's supervisor. The only reason one brother was excluded from the intervention was because he and my mother had an incredible amount of anger toward each other and I predicted the intervention would have turned into a boxing match, just as the first few family sessions eventually did. Also my older brother was, unfortunately, one of the scapegoats in the family and his presence could easily have shifted the focus away from my mother.

Our group met the night before the intervention for a trial run. We each had our list of hurts that my mother had caused us because of her drinking and we read off our lists as if my mother were actually there. Her supervisor led the intervention. We each said our piece and then at the end the leader gave my mother the ultimatum. She told her that her place in the hospital was already set up for her and that she would go straight from the intervention to the hospital for treatment and her job would be there for her when she got back. We would have her suitcase packed and with us with all the things she'd need and she'd have no choice but to go to the hospital which was just a few blocks away from her office.

We met in an empty conference room in her building at 2 P.M. on the day of the intervention. We were all nervous and jittery, but my mother seemed very calm when she walked in and saw us all sitting there. She was not shocked by any means, at least she didn't appear shocked, though later she said she had never been so shocked in her life. She said when she walked into the conference room and saw all of us sitting there she was sure someone had died and we had come to convey the news.

During the intervention she started sobbing. It was so sad to see her like that, but it was sadder to see her

187

drunk and self-destructing. She was not defensive. She couldn't be. After living with an alcoholic long enough, one has enough evidence for confrontation. Each of us had at least a half a dozen memories of her destructive drunken binges, and they were read off, one by one, at that table:

"On Christmas Eve you'd scream all night and then not be able to get up on Christmas morning."

"The time I had to take that really important test in the morning and I couldn't sleep all night because of your screaming until five in the morning."

"When I was in grammar school and you showed up to my basketball games drunk and embarrassed me in front of everyone."

"When you beat me up because I came in one minute late. You were bombed and you pulled my hair out of my head."

Pretty soon my turn came. I remembered what the priest told me when he was giving me the information about the intervention. He had said: "Don't forget to tell your mother you love her. She needs to hear that." And though I felt ambivalence about that at the time, I managed to be able to say that because I did also feel it was needed. So I started by saying: "I just want to tell you before I read my list that I love you and I'm only doing this because I really want you to get the help you deserve. I want to see you well." Then I read:

"You married Harry and let him live with us and abuse us for all that time. And all the nights you drank and never came home. You got drunk at my high school graduation party. You were drunk the morning I was leaving for the army. You couldn't get out of bed to say good-bye."

Annie's turn came. She was the youngest, fifteen years old, and she had a hard time reading the list she wrote. She sat next to me with her head on the table throughout the whole confrontation, crying hysterically. She asked me the night before if I would read her list for her. On her list she had, "The night you hit me with the baseball bat and I had to go to school with a black eye." She sobbed louder and louder as I read.

My mother went straight from the intervention to the hospital notwithstanding her desperate, but useless attempts to delay entry, and the rest of us attended Family Therapy on a weekly basis. Luckily I was legally assigned to a base in Brooklyn for a few months, despite my commander's unwillingness to cooperate on this matter. She had no control over it because I was cleared by the officials at Fort Hamilton, Brooklyn.

The intervention itself was the easiest part of the whole ordeal. The pain had only just begun, not only for my mother, but for me as well. Family Therapy turned out to be a bit more than I bargained for. I was not emotionally prepared to deal with some of the issues that came up. What I learned in Family Therapy was that my family was as dense and denying of their problems as I had been of mine all my life and that I was now incompatible with them because I had already been in recovery. Why I didn't expect that was my own lack of readiness to come to terms with all of the effects of alcoholism, not only on my own life, but on my entire family's. I was, however, incredibly aware of both my own struggles and my family's denial of illness and I was incapable at that point, of letting go and allowing them to grow and change at their own pace. I feared they would never grow unless I enlightened them. I was overwhelmingly frustrated over the growing realization that they were not going to see things my way.

They were blind as far as I was concerned; not to everything, of course, but definitely to the manifestations of alcoholism in their own lives and personalities.

The family sessions generated a tremendous amount of anger and rage in me as long forgotten memories began to spring out of my unconscious, setting my consciousness on fire. Happenings which I thought seemed so insignificant before now started to saturate my thinking. As I sat and listened to each person in the family struggle to defend themselves and their behavior I started to relive the past.

My mother was talking: "I did the best I could to provide for six kids. It was a heavy burden to be left with. Thank God you kids always had clothes on your backs, and food on the table, and beds to sleep in at night. And you all went through good Catholic schools. Do you think that was easy?"

And my mind drifted back as she spoke, back to when I was in the fourth grade. She was drinking very heavily then and all the people living in our building whom we described as "lowlifes" somehow found their way to our dining room table where they'd sit, sipping on Manhattans. Around that time I remember all the girls in my class came to school with these marshmallow shoes. It was the new fad, a sandal with a three- or four-inch platform rubber sole. I wanted a pair of those shoes so badly, but Mom wouldn't buy them for me. She had no time so I stole some money from her purse to buy myself a pair.

I immediately ran down to Buster Brown's on Broadway. I told the man I wanted a pair of marshmallow shoes. He measured my foot and brought out a pair on sale. I tried them on. They were too big. My feet were sliding around in them, but I insisted on having them and I only had enough money to buy them on sale. So I took the shoes, ran home, and wore them to school the next day. When I walked into the classroom, late, I made my way down the aisle between the fourth and fifth row of desks, and all the girls in the rows started laughing at my shoes. I was so awkward walking in them that they reacted right away. One girl yelled out, "Denise! Your shoes are two different colors," and everyone laughed. They were two different colors, two different shades of brown. I noticed it when I purchased them, but I hoped no one else would notice. I walked home in my marshmallow sandals that afternoon feeling as if I were walking the cement-paved streets in a pair of ski boots, swearing all the while never to wear those ugly things again. But that did not erase the shame and humiliation of having already been seen in them and of still having them unwantedly strapped around my feet.

I never did wear those sandals again. One of my mother's strange friends, a woman I didn't want in my home, but somehow always appeared there, bought them from me for a couple of dollars. They did seem to fit her feet better than mine, but they were still two different colors. I was glad she could not alter this defect. I liked the idea of her wearing something I hated and I even thought that maybe people would laugh at her the way they did me. As far as I was concerned she deserved to be laughed at because she made herself at home in my apartment, knowing full well she was not welcome there by me, or by any of my brothers and sisters.

"You kids are lucky, you know," I heard again from my mother's mouth. My mind traveled back even further, back to the third grade. . . . I wanted to go out and play with the other kids, but she wouldn't let me leave the apartment. I screamed and screamed and then I acted out a false surrender. I pretended I was giving up and I quieted down long enough to get my mother off the defensive. As soon as I sensed she was relaxing in the safety of my surrender, I made a mad dash for the door and flew down the five flights of stairs and out onto the street. We were living in a small two-bedroom apartment then (we didn't move to the four-bedroom project until a few years after my father died). Once I achieved my objective and made it to the street, I felt awful. This sense of guilt and sheer terror infested my heart and I couldn't stay out and play with the other kids because I was afraid if I stayed out my mother would beat the pulp out of me when I returned. So I ran back inside, and up the stairs. I knocked on the door and then backed away so she couldn't just grab me in a fit of anger. When she opened the door I said, "I'm sorry! I came back! Please, I didn't mean it! Please! Are you gonna hit me? I'm sorry, Mommy."

"No," she said. "I'm not gonna touch you. Just get in here now."

"You won't hit me?"

"No. Not if you get in here right now. Come on in and I won't touch you."

So I cautiously crept through the door, ready at any moment to make a run for the bathroom. But she was quicker than I expected, and she was hiding a broom behind the door. She slammed the door shut behind me, grabbed me by my shirt and started smacking me with the handle end of the broom. Then she dragged me into the small bedroom where my sister and I slept in the double bed. She shoved me on the inside so she could block the door. She wasn't going to leave me alone because I would run to the bathroom, lock myself in and scream bloody hell for the rest of the night. She knew the routine, and she didn't want to hear it.

She held me hostage for the entire night. She lay on the side of the bed closest to the door, and every time I budged, she rolled over and smashed me in the face. I saw flashes of little stars amidst the blackness which accompanied each blow. She was afraid that when I moved, I was attempting to escape to the bathroom, even when I was just moving because my body was aching from lying in one position. I hated her big ugly body lying next to mine, and I hated her anger-crazed eyes.

I never escaped that night. It was about five in the morning when she finally left the room. She thought I was asleep. I was awake, though, and I contemplated making a dash for the bathroom so I could scream for hours on end and she would have lost the battle. But I just couldn't do it. I was so exhausted, really worn out. My body felt limp and lifeless. So I kept my eyes closed and did fall off to sleep. When we went to my aunt's house the next day, my aunt saw the massive bruise which covered my entire thigh. She asked me, "Denise, what happened to your leg?"

Angrily I said, "My mother beat me with the broom." My mother turned around and said, "I did not." And that was the end of it.

All my mother's lip service about how lucky we were because all our needs were met, made me want to gag, to vomit in the middle of the circle we were sitting in. I hated her, but I felt so bad for her because she was so sick. What a dilemma. She had deprived us of everything because she deprived us of her time, her attention, and her love. But I couldn't hate her now as I sat there seventeen years later. I could not hate her. All I could do was walk out of the family session and continue to feel alienated from the world, and to destroy every relationship I managed to get started. I could not have normal, healthy relationships with other people. I always wound up hating them, resenting them, abusing them, or losing interest in them. But, my mother? I couldn't hate her. I felt terribly sorry for her. She had a hard life.

I was terrified because I was so intensely enraged and it was seeping out of me in every area of my life. I brought this anger to AA meetings, I brought it to work with me, and I brought it to bed with me. I had no peace for those couple of months and I was haunted by this gnawing pain inside me which wouldn't go away, and I couldn't figure out, either, how to get rid of it or how to deal with it. It was horrifying, so horrifying that I regressed to crunching up in my little ball again. If I became angry over some real or imagined problem at work, I would withdraw and fall asleep on the floor where no one would find me, often in the back of the chapel where I worked at Fort Hamilton, or in one of the pews when the church was empty. I began to feel very lonely and very sick again. Continuing to attend family therapy was feeding the anger because it was a constant reminder of my buried past. All the pain of childhood, of growing up practically parentless, of being labeled the "crazy" one in the family, of being the underdog among my peers in grammar school and the bully in high school, of being the kid who felt like crawling under the desk in the first grade because she pissed in her seat, of being the kid who was whipped out of bed in the middle of the night to be beaten to a pulp by a drunken man who was welcomed by her mother in her home, of being the kid who had to get tough or die of humiliation.

All that surfaced, however, was anger, fear, and this pervading sense of uselessness about continuing to live. I was entering into another dimension of recovery on a much deeper level. My recovery, thus far, had touched upon my past, but primarily centered on staying away from the first drink and learning how to deal with daily problems more responsibly. Now I was getting into the unidentified, confused, jumbled, suppressed feelings of growing up in an alcoholic home and also, my present alienation from my family.

My mother stayed dry for a little while after she got out of the hospital, how long I don't know, but it wasn't too long before she was back on the sauce. This had been her third or fourth trip through the hospital for her alcoholism, yet she still didn't catch on. She continued to see a social worker on a weekly basis, the same one who worked with her when she was an in-patient. She continued to bluff the social worker about her drinking and she was adamant about not needing AA meetings. Her social worker, unfortunately, focused more on my mother's depression than her alcoholism. I found that utterly frustrating since I knew my mother's drinking problem inside out, probably better than I knew my own. It was her alcoholism that needed treatment first! All the same, my mother's being in the hospital and receiving treatment rekindled my hope that maybe one day we would be sitting together in an AA meeting and maybe we could share recovery since we spent such a long time sharing the illness.

I boarded the plane for Germany just two hours after our last family session. I felt a false unity with my family, sort of a temporary bond which I allowed to exist because it would help me survive their presence. The gap between us was far and wide, too far and too wide.

The whole family took a cab with me from the hospital to the airport and I was on my way back to Frankfurt to finish my tour of duty with the army. I had only eight months left before I would be finished with my three-year commitment. I was more than anxious to get finished. My military commitment was keeping me from the access to further therapy which I desperately needed. I didn't know exactly where I could get the help to continue my journey to health, but I did know the terrifying reality that it was going to get worse. I had only scratched the surface. My personality was weak, fragile and distorted, and this would show up eventually in every pursuit I undertook. It was going to take years to undo the damage of my past, damage which manifested itself in my twisted, enmeshed view of reality, my disconnectedness from the human family.

Twenty
Back from New York

I had lived out my commander's greatest fear when I did not return to my unit as scheduled. She took my legal extension in New York as a personal attack, purposely carried out against her and so she came to regard me as the challenging enemy. For this reason, she was anxious to have me incarcerated.

Lt. Kinderson called me into her office and told me I had an appointment with an army lawyer concerning a pending Article 15, the military's non-judicial punishment system, from an incident I had with a sergeant before I left for New York. I had had an altercation with a sergeant who was in charge of me for staff duty one Sunday morning. She was angry because I showed no guilt or remorse for showing up to work forty-five minutes late, and I was angry because she appeared hung over on the job and I could have gotten high on her breath alone. Tension built between us over the hours and she began to order me around in the devaluing way she had every right to because she was a sergeant and I was a private first class. When I refused to pick up the clumps of grass scattered around the battalion grounds because it was pouring outside and I had already spent a good portion of the morning beautifying the grounds upon command, Sergeant Bloodshot relieved me of duty and wrote me up for disobeying orders. She recommended me for an Article 15, which Lt. Kinderson had taken most seriously, and was now reminding me about with such a self-assuredness that I had to suspect she was most pleased by my ability to set myself up and thus allow her this opportunity to punish me. While Sgt. Bloodshot was busy writing me up, I was busy writing her up—but instead of recommending her for an Article 15, I recommended her for free counseling at Frankfurt Communications and a psychiatric evaluation.

After refreshing my memory about my offenses Lt. Kinderson informed me I was the alternate mail clerk for the Christmas holidays. Her manner was unusually relaxed and agreeable toward me. She even told me to have a seat in her office.

A few days later, I was called into her office again. Her attitude had taken a drastic turn for the worse. I figured she was experiencing frustration in some area of her life. It was hard to believe that I could be the sole source of her fury. She reiterated, very sternly this time, that I had an appointment with an army lawyer and I was not to miss it. Her facial expression was tight and rigid. She told me only to listen and not to say a word. I think it bothered her that I obliged.

Not long after that meeting I was called in again and I was instructed not to say a word except "Yes, Ma'am." Then she asked me if I understood. I responded as ordered: "Yes, Ma'am." Lt. Kinderson explained to me that the next time something like this happened with me (referring to the incident with Sgt. Bloodshot), she was going to recommend me for a chapter out of the military. Then she asked me if I understood. I actually was quite confused. For this reason I did not respond "Yes, Ma'am," and because I did not want to disrespect her by saying anything other than "Yes, Ma'am," I did not respond at all.

Lt. Kinderson's blood pressure rose tremendously. Her face flushed and her eyes hardened and locked. She was so disturbed that I could see an involuntary pulselike movement just beside her right eyebrow. It was the only movement that let me know she was still alive. She maintained a statue-like pose until she moved her lips, barely, to speak. Her eyes looked like two bullets ready to fire out of their sockets with but the slightest pressure on the trigger. My mouth was the trigger. She repeated, so loudly that I was sure our private conversation was being heard all over building 402, "Do you understand, Ranaghan!" I did not want to disobey her order so I did not respond. Then Lt. Kinderson took a deep breath and let up slightly, "Okay, Ranaghan, you can say 'Yes, Ma'am' or 'No, Ma'am.' Do you understand, Ranaghan?"

The questioning tone had returned to take the place of the demanding tone. I answered, with my new-found freedom, "No, Ma'am." She then asked me what it was I did not understand. I could not fit that into a "Yes, Ma'am or" a "No, Ma'am" so I stood silently, responding in my unresponsiveness.

She asked me again, this time slowly and very carefully dragging out every word, "Whaaat didn'ttttt youuuu und-er-stand, Ranaghan?"

I could not respond with either of my choices.

She continued (her body was fully functioning again. It had slowly rolled out of the statue pose). "Okay; do you understand the word **the,** Ranaghan?"

I responded, "Yes, Ma'am."

Next she asked me, "Do you understand the word **next,** Ranaghan?"

I responded, "Yes, Ma'am."

Then she asked me, "Do you understand the word **time,** Ranaghan?"

I answered, No, Ma'am." I was curious to see what would happen if I opted for the unexpected response.

Maybe Lt. Kinderson would ask me, "What don't you understand about the word **time,** Ranaghan?" Then upon realizing I could not respond to that with a "Yes, Ma'am" or a "No, Ma'am," she might add a third response option for me and I would feel we were progressing toward individual empowerment. However, it didn't happen as I had wished it to. Lt. Kinderson was incredibly angry. She leaned forward over her desk, came to a half-standing position and ordered me out of her office: "You're not insane, Ranaghan! You just like to play head games with people. You are very intelligent. You play head games and I'm not going to take it anymore. You act like an idiot! Get out of my office!"

"Yes, Ma'am," I responded. I stood motionless, saluting her for what seemed like minutes because she was reluctant to return the salute, and I left the office.

I did make my appointment with the lawyer and having had that out of the way, Lt. Kinderson was free to read me my rights and decide upon my punishment for being disrespectful to an NCO. She gave me 32 hours extra duty, restriction to the barracks for a month, a reduction from Specialist to Private First Class. In addition to this, she was thoughtful enough to schedule me an appointment with the psychiatrist. She ignored my recommendation for a psychiatric evaluation for Sgt. Bloodshot despite the chaos that developed while I was on leave as a result of Sgt. Bloodshot's drinking. Sgt. Bloodshot had been picked up for driving while intoxicated. But not to worry; nobody died . . . that time.

My punishment was quite harsh for a first time offender such as myself. I spent many an afternoon scrubbing and buffing the floor in the orderly room. It looked worse when I finished with it than when I started, because the mop I used to spread the wax was dirty, so I was buffing dirty wax into the clean floor, not realizing what I was doing until it was already done. I spent most of my extra duty time scraping the dirty wax off the clean floor and it just never did look very good when I finished.

When I completed serving my extra duty hours, Lt. Kinderson had her clerk redo the floor I had endlessly labored over. I had actually started to care about the floor I was cleaning. It was something I had been working on for so long and I started to take a little pride in it, despite the fact that I was doing it under direct orders. I wanted the floor to come out looking okay. Again it was as if I did a good job and the floor looked okay, then maybe that meant I was okay. The floor was a reflection of me. I was intimately connected to its appearance. Unfortunately, the floor didn't look okay when I was finished with it. The wax, which was supposed to add a beautiful, thick, shiny layer to the floor and invite praise and compliments from others, instead, added a layer of dirt; it invited criticism, and even laughter.

In addition to my punishments, Lt. Kinderson began threatening me left and right with Article 15's. She also threatened to throw me in jail or send me to a confinement facility for women, even though she had absolutely no basis to do so. But I did take her threats seriously because I had seen some very strange things happen, both in and out of the military. Once again, someone was threatening to send me away because they believed that I was a hopeless case, out of their control and utterly intolerable.

Lt. Kinderson began to treat me as if I were insane. She had trouble deciding whether I was a rebel or a mental case. She would have conversations about me with other people while I was standing right in front of her.

She ignored me, as if I were deaf, unable to comprehend her words, or even as if I were non-existent.

I was very unhappy in my unit, as anyone with even the smallest amount of pride might be. I talked regularly to Mr. Sherwood about it and I spent as much time as I could hanging around the RTF as it was my refuge. Mr. Sherwood and I decided it would be worth a try to ask LTC Hazy if I could get transferred to the RTF and work as a clerk there. So I presented this to LTC Hazy and his attitude toward this idea seemed very positive. He was willing to allow me to work at the RTF and spoke with Dr. McMann, the director of the RTF, about it over the phone.

However, not much later, LTC Hazy took a sudden turn in this positive attitude and he dropped the consideration of my transfer like a hot potato refusing to discuss it with me at all. I figured he had brought the issue to the Brigade Commander, who decided I had already caused enough trouble and enough paper work by extending my leave in New York. I imagined he thought he must be responsible and put a stop to this private's constant need to make herself the exception, "the one who's trying to manipulate the system to suit herself instead of suiting herself to the system. She stays right where she is."

But something else was going on now with the administration and LTC Hazy too. In fact, I was beginning to feel that this tension, which initially, I only felt between Lt. Kinderson and myself, was spreading among the chain of command. Conflicts between myself and others were escalating at an alarming rate.

I worked in the section just across the hall from LTC Hazy's office. He was always around and up until the time of my request to transfer to work at the hospital, I was familiar and comfortable with his presence. LTC Hazy, one afternoon a few weeks after my request had been rejected, was acting as he always had with me. He came into my section, and after a friendly greeting, said he wanted to show me a picture of his old driver. He called me: "Ranaghan, come here. Did you see that picture of Born Bad?" I followed him into his office across the hall, not wanting to, but feeling obligated. As I passed the 1SG from the unit we shared the building with, he screamed at me, "WATCH WHERE YOU'RE WALKING, PRIVATE! LOOK AT THAT! SHE WALKS RIGHT BY US—ALMOST BUMPS INTO US!" LTC Hazy came out with the picture of Born Bad which he was infatuated with, and proceeded to explain the picture to me. I said, very low and insincere since it all seemed fake, "That's nice" and began to walk away. 1SG Stalk was still standing there. He looked at me as I walked by and again, he began to scream at me: "GET OVER HERE, RANAGHAN! WHO DO YOU THINK YOU ARE, WALKING PAST US LIKE THAT! WHO'S YOUR SUPERVISOR!"

"SFC Hardy," I answered and then quickly corrected myself with, "No, SSG Dinger." I had gone brain-dead for a few seconds, because I was shocked that I was getting screamed at for walking by, and I had forgotten an intermediary supervisor was recently assigned to me to make the communication between myself and SFC Hardy less frequent.

1SG Stalk said, "Huh! She doesn't even know who her supervisor is. Let's go get SSG Dinger and have a little talk!"

I looked 1SG Stalk in the eye and this seemed to aggravate him further: "Get out of my face, Ranaghan, and get out of my way!" He stormed down the hall in a fury after he yelled again, "Get out of my way, Private!" He practically knocked me over to get past me because I didn't move fast enough. He caught SSG Dinger by surprise when he ordered her to get up and go to the conference room for a session. She was confused, but jumped up to the sound of Sgt. Stalk's voice and double-timed into the conference room. Once in the conference room he slammed the door shut and began ranting: "You are a private! I am a sergeant!" Then he turned to SFC Dinger and continued; "This private thinks she can do and say anything she wants." Then he turned to me and screamed; "Well, this is one sergeant you are not going to mess around with!"

He went on making noise for a few more minutes and told me I could not respond, only "Yes, I understand, Sergeant." *Déjà vu,* I thought.

When he asked me if I understood, I did not want to lie, and having been conditioned from my earlier interaction with Lt. Kinderson, I knew standing there silently was not a good choice. So I was honest and told him I did not understand and he went crazy: "Don't play that crap with me, Ranaghan! You play stupid—well don't pull that with *me!*"

Then he gave me a direct order. He said, "Go ahead and smile, Ranaghan." I did as I was told and forced a stiff, very unnatural smile. He turned to SSG Dinger and asked her, "Did you see that, SSG Dinger! Did you see that!" SSG Dinger, now torn between being confused or being intimidated, wobbled her head up and down and all around.

1SG Stalk then threatened me with UCMJ action and said he was going to the sergeant major about me. I wasn't surprised. By this time I'd been hearing UCMJ-UCMJ-UCMJ in my dreams on a regular basis. UCMJ is the army's Uniform Code of Military Justice.

1SG Stalk and I began to have similar encounters

more frequently. One afternoon I refused to give one of the sergeants from 1SG Stalk's unit his mail because the mail room hours were posted on the door and it was not time to give mail out. I was still busy distributing it into boxes and I was simply following the rules which were laid down for me to follow. The soldier got very irate, though, and stormed off to get 1SG Stalk. When he arrived he asked me what the problem was and I explained that there wasn't a problem at all, that I was putting the mail out and at 3 P.M. the sergeant could come and pick up his package just like everybody else.

1SG Stalk appeared to be listening patiently, but I had a hunch he was just timing his response. Something in his bulging, anxious eyes told me he was up to something else. He was being too nice and that was never his temperament. Just as I was beginning to sense something fishy about this, I stopped explaining myself and it came like a tornado. Suddenly 1SG Stalk turned a deaf ear and began to accuse me of not wanting to serve the soldiers!

"You have an attitude problem, Ranaghan; and we are going to have a meeting with the commander and the mail room officer!" When I agreed that was an excellent idea, an opportunity to discuss the problems, maybe change the mail room hours so it would better serve the soldier and the mail room clerk, 1SG Stalk began to speak with a threatening undertone: "We'll see, Ranaghan. I think you just like to cause trouble." And he walked away.

I had had trouble before this, working in the mail room when CPT Ramos was the commander of the same unit 1SG was from. He seemed to think he could walk into the mail room any time he wanted to just because he was the commander. It was against the rules to allow anyone in the mail room, other than the mail room officer, and the other mail clerks. CPT Ramos thought it absurd for a private to ask him to remove himself from a place he didn't belong. He aggressively informed me that he could do anything he wanted while he reminded me again, that I was a private.

I was continuously getting in trouble for doing what I thought was the right thing to do. I brought these incidences to LTC Hazy because I felt I was being verbally abused and there were no grounds for it (as if there are ever, any grounds for abuse). LTC Hazy took the fatherly role and said he would talk to CPT Ramos and it wouldn't happen again. In the meantime, CPT Ramos had found out I had gone to the battalion commander and so he was busily persuading SPC Tipper, the other mail room clerk, to defend him by trying to convince Tipper that he only entered the mail room to perform inspections. Both Tipper and I knew that CPT Ramos came in the mail room only to inspect and remove his personal packages from the shelf, but Tipper wasn't quite sure that speaking the truth, which was not in favor of the commander, was the wisest thing to do. And while LTC Hazy was promising this wouldn't happen again, it happened again, in LTC Hazy's presence. When LTC came in for his mail and spotted CPT Ramos barging through the mail room door, he told him to get out. But CPT Ramos didn't hear very well because he made his way through the door and made no motion to leave. And again, LTC Hazy was laughing, as if this was a joke. I realized, more clearly than before, that LTC Hazy thought I was a joke. When I had told him in the meeting I had with him, that CPT Ramos attacked me for no reason, he answered, "Oh, that's just his way of dealing with it. Everyone has a different style."

Twenty-one
Onward

Lt. Kinderson was still in command when I returned to Germany. She only lasted six months as commander, but before she relinquished her command, she referred me back to Psychiatry, back to Dr. Cambridge whom I hadn't visited in well over a year. She asked him to please recommend a discharge if possible. She explained to Dr. Cambridge that I was just back after having spent three months in New York and I seemed to have some difficulties readjusting to the unit. I met with Dr. Cambridge, and when I did, he was adamant about refusing to recommend I be discharged because I only had five months of service left. His attitude was that of a proud father, impressed that I had survived so long against the odds, and so I was surprised when he ended the session and then wrote up the following:

> Based upon this evaluation, the diagnostic impression is: Mixed personality disorder, severe with borderline schizotypal, and antisocial features. This condition is a deeply ingrained, maladaptive pattern of behavior of long duration which interferes with the soldier's ability to perform duty. The disorder is so severe that the soldier's ability to function effectively in the military environment is significantly impaired. Discharge IAW AR 625-200 paragraph 5-13 is recommended. This soldier is psychiatrically cleared for any administrative action deemed appropriate by command.

My commander, then Lt. Kinderson, joyfully informed me of this recommendation immediately upon receiving it. Her spirit resembled that of a law student who just received notice that she passed her bar exam.

I returned to Dr. Cambridge's busy office, uninvited, and expressed my disgust with his recommendation. I insisted he retract his letter.

"I do not have the authority to chapter you out of the military," he said. "All I can do is recommend a chapter. Your commander doesn't have to follow my recommendation. It's up to administration to put you out of the service. Your unit is putting you out of the service, not me."

"But you said you wouldn't recommend I be chaptered, remember? Quote: 'You made it this far. You can make it five more months!'"

"Yes, but I cannot deny you have a personality disorder. You do have a personality disorder."

Here we go again, I thought to myself. *Another jerk going by his fat books, disregarding the circumstances, ignoring my feelings and opinions because I am not in a position to speak.*

"I cannot believe you. You lied to me. They are putting me out of the military because you, a psychiatrist, who is supposed to be wise and competent, whose opinion is highly valued, recommended it. How could you do that? How could you lie to me!"

I must have miraculously struck a chord somewhere in Dr. Cambridge because he did retract his letter about three weeks later. He did two things. He put me into a weekly group therapy with other soldiers who had abusive histories and now were having trouble in the service. The group was geared toward trying to find the connection between the abuse from our past and our present adjustment problems. Looking back on the group now, I feel it was too analytical to serve the purpose of solving our immediate problem of adjusting to the military. Deeply rooted issues were dredged up and familiar feelings of intolerable loneliness arose. I found myself feeling left alone with them and my mental state quickly decompensating. There was no individual therapy available.

The second thing Dr. Cambridge did was to write a second letter to my commander:

PFC Ranaghan has been known to the Psychiatry Department here since 13 February 1987. From 17 March 1987 until 1 December 1988 she was not seen in our clinic. On 1 December 1988 I saw her at her commanding officer's request. Later that day I told her commanding officer that the diagnosis of Personality Disorder is obvious and that I would recommend separation IAW AR 635-200 paragraph 5-13. I added, and I quote from my notes ". . . but a waiting period might be in order because E3 Ranaghan might improve her behavior with therapy. . . ."

Since 1 December 1988 PFC Ranaghan has been in a new type of weekly group therapy. She shows improvement in her mood, in her social behavior, and possibly in her duty performance. In my opinion it might be beneficial to the army to continue PFC Ranaghan in the army at least several more weeks on a trial basis to see if she can maintain an acceptable performance level.

It was 6:30 A.M. on a Monday morning when the knock came on my barracks door. It was Specialist Manley: "Ranaghan, the first sergeant wants to see you in his office ASAP."

"Sure. Thanks. I'll be right down."

I threw on a pair of sweat pants and sneakers and walked down the steps to the orderly room in the basement. The first sergeant was talking to someone and

209

when he finished, he looked up and saw me standing in front of his desk. He put down the papers that he had in his hands and began to speak:

"Ranaghan, I hate to be the one to tell you this, but your paperwork came back approved. The decision was made by the brigade commander to chapter you out of the military for having a personality disorder."

"When do I leave?"

"As soon as possible. You start outprocessing today. You don't have to worry about going to work at the gym. I'll call them and let them know you won't be working there anymore. You start clearing today. SSG Dinger will be taking you to outprocess. You have to have an escort."

"Why do I have to have an escort? I think I can find my way around just fine."

"All chapter cases have to have an escort, Ranaghan. And you have to be in full uniform too. Why don't you go upstairs and get dressed and be back down here at 0800 hours."

After two long weeks of outprocessing, which consisted of turning in uniforms and equipment and signing papers left and right, I was headed back to New York. Before I left I made one last attempt to have the opportunity to finish my time in the service. I felt I had struggled long and hard to survive in the military environment and I had managed to adjust for two and one-half years. Now, with five months of service left, I was being put out? I wrote a letter to the V Corps General and personally delivered it to his headquarters, asking him please to consider my case. A woman from the church I attended knew the secretary to the General and she called her to let her know I would be coming by with it. This was a guarantee the letter would get to the General's desk, rather than tossed among the junk mail.

The day my goods were supposed to be picked up from the shipping company I was informed that the General had reviewed my packet and decided that it would be best if I were chaptered. The next morning at 0500 hrs. I was on my way to the airport.

I really hadn't expected the paperwork to go through. I had a good mind for blocking out, until the very end, the reality of the situation because of my new belief that "anything is possible." A newly recovering individual often has tremendous faith in those words. But because I blocked out that there was even a chance I might be put out of the military, I hadn't processed any of the feelings that would have been brought about by this outcome. I experienced my rejection as a shock rather than as an inevitable ending. I felt a mixed bag of very powerful feelings.

I felt anger. I told myself: "Why should I have to suffer this gross injustice because of incompetent, power-hungry, egotistical morons? After all, I hadn't exhausted the non-judicial punishment system. I only had one Article 15 on my record. A few steps are definitely missing. My discharge was an impulsive decision made by someone who felt threatened enough by me to want to get rid of me. And I'm powerless, fighting alone, against a system infinitely more powerful than myself."

I also felt revenge: "I am writing to Washington, D.C., and the Senate and the Congress will hear about every drunk in this unit, including the battalion commander!"

A part of me felt relief: "Well, I'm getting out of this 'shithole' a little early. I don't have to deal with it anymore. Maybe this is God's will for me. I was never happy here anyway."

And I felt depressed: "I have failed again. I have been victimized again. I always seem to be in the position where I can be kicked around. And I have no place to go, no place I really want to be."

I outprocessed at Fort Dix, New Jersey. It was a snowy, cold Friday morning. I stayed on the post until Monday morning. I was the last one to leave the barracks from our group of outprocessees. Everyone else was raring to get out as quickly as possible. For two nights I was the only one on the second floor of the barracks. Nobody knew I was there, not even the security guards whose thumping footsteps I heard as they passed by my room on their nightly rounds. All the other former soldiers caught their buses or had relatives pick them up. I was very quiet about leaving. I didn't have any place that I was anxious to get to. The bitter ending of my painful military career left me feeling down, defeated. It was more the sting of having been stripped of my dignity than anything else. *The military has a way of doing that to people,* I thought.

I woke up early on a bitter cold snowy Monday morning at Fort Dix. I was very aware of people going to work and looking busy. I was not busy. It felt good to be able to sit back and watch, knowing I was free. No one was expecting me to be anywhere at any time. I heard the basic trainees jogging by at 5 A.M. It brought back a flood of memories and I was endlessly grateful that I was not one of them. I thought to myself: *You have to be one of two ways to survive in basic training: You either have to love yourself and have so much confidence in yourself that you are unaffected by what the drill sergeants say and do to you, so you can go about performing the mission unharmed, or you have to have such a low opinion of yourself that you believe what they say to you is true and then that does not bother you either.* I had this snapshot in my head of my platoon in basic training and I saw us as a group of young, vulnerable, directionless, lost souls, looking for the military to provide us with some kind of reason for being.

I trudged through the snow over to the legal assistance office on Fort Dix and asked one last time if there was anything they could do for me to help me finish my tour right there on Fort Dix. I laughed to myself at my persistence because I knew the struggle was long over. I had already been discharged, and upon realizing this, I wondered when I was going to get strong enough so that I wouldn't have to get jerked around so much in this society.

I waited for a military taxi outside of the legal office and took the taxi to the bus depot. I was home within two hours on Monday.

I didn't want to be home, too many bad memories and broken dreams. But I had no place to go but home, back to that 14th floor apartment in the Bronx project. The dented paper-thin walls reeked of violence and dripped with despair, depression and abuse. I hadn't lived at home in seven years. Returning to it felt like regression. I was panic-stricken at the realization that after all I'd been through I wound up back there. It was so much the same. The people dwelling in it also seemed too much the same. I would have to survive in this atmosphere until I was equipped with the tools to build my own space in this world.

I asked God: "Okay, God, what do you want me to do with my life?" And nothing swelled up within. No definite answer appeared written across my forehead. No bolt of lightning struck me. No opportunity knocked at my door, and no job was waiting for Denise Marie Patricia Ranaghan to take over.

At the same time I realized these disappointing factors, I also realized that my life would go on and things would happen and there would be some things I would have to knock for and some things I would have to wait for. And there would be some things I would knock for and wait for and still never have. But my life would go on. Good times and bad times all would pass, and then soon, I would find that I had some things, good and bad, which I never knocked for or waited for . . . because that's just the way life is sometimes.

Through all the suffering I had somehow managed to discover that love does exist, and that is truly the greatest discovery of all. If I were to live forever without ever feeling the gentle hands of love, my life would be a total waste. But having had even just a few encounters with people who love provided enough reason for me to say that life was worth living. Of course I would need much more than a few encounters with the people of love. I would need many, but at least I knew what I needed. I knew what was missing. I discovered love through people like Mr. Sherwood and Lt. Sharples. It only takes one caring person to reach down into, and illuminate, a dark soul.

Having come to terms with the fact that I am an addict and my answer was not to be found in a bottle of wine, and I do have an emotional illness which will require my attention to heal, and that I was not born to be a soldier of war, I now feel freer to come to terms with my inner self, my soul, a process I was fortunate to begin in the army. When I left the military, I anticipated that hard times lay ahead for me. This I thought of not in the sense of a destructive, foolish, self-fulfilling prophecy, but rather, as an acknowledgment of the pain and anguish endured by one human soul struggling out of a dark black hole, in an attempt to be truly and fully transformed in the light.

Epilogue

I entered the military in July 1986 and was discharged in February 1989. I entered the military on an impulse because I needed the quickest escape from myself and from what I perceived as an intolerable family situation. Ironically, my escape into the service turned out to be the only escape which brought me, full circle, around to myself. Instead of losing myself, as I had done so many times before, I found myself, and in a sense, this meant that my running days were over. Escaping from myself is now an impossibility. All attempts to escape are short-lived and temporary. I don't credit the military system for this enlightenment. I credit the special individuals I encountered while I was in the military, some of them soldiers and some of them civilians.

A few major contributing factors which led to my decompensation in the military were: my refusal to ingest alcohol or drugs in order to pacify myself; a personal history of abuse which the military environment, in many ways, felt like a re-creation of; a genetic predisposition to major depression; a very weak and sometimes false sense of self; and an inability to feel connected with human beings.

Coming to terms with my scarred, and in many ways, lost childhood, is a gruelingly slow process. I thought the lows I hit in the military were the worst I could possibly experience. They weren't. Life got worse for me and it became increasingly difficult for me to convince myself it was worth hanging around for. Many therapists I went to for consultation refused to treat me. I got fired from my first post-military job and I cycled in and out of emergency rooms and psychiatric wards for the next five years. At times I was severely depressed. I attempted suicide more than once. But I suppose if I really wanted to die I would have done so by now. I'm still here.

In late 1989, when I was unable to work or maintain housing for myself, I was referred by the BxVA to a long-term in-patient treatment program at the New York Psychiatric Institute. This program saved my life. I remained in the program for two and a half years. During the latter part of my stay at the Psychiatric Institute I began taking courses at Teachers College, Columbia University, and I have since earned by Ed.M. in psychological counseling.

The next obstacle I was to face after my discharge from PI and my graduation from TC was employment. I had great difficulty maintaining it. My rage and my abandonment issues continued to interfere with my work in organizations. I was starting jobs and at the same time estimating how long it would take before I'd "get fired from this one." It never took more than a few months. The greatest gift I have received as a consequence of being fired continuously, is that I have learned the art of handling rejection. Rejection and failure no longer frighten me, paralyze me, or drive me to self-destructive behavior. I find a lesson in all experiences.

I take medication for depression and I am no longer plagued with thoughts of suicide. I presently live in a studio apartment in the Bronx, with my three cats and my three dogs, and I work as a resident manager in a home for developmentally disabled persons. I am hoping that this position will be a positive experience.

So what's the reward for riding this treacherous road toward wholeness: true peace and satisfaction in knowing the resilient spirit that lives inside myself . . . in knowing that I, and each one of us, truly is a lovable child existing on this universe for a purpose, whether that purpose be known or, as yet, unrevealed.